Scott Foresman - Addison Wesley

MIDDLE SCHOOL MATH

Course 2

User's Guide
to accompany

TestWorks™
Test and Practice Software

Test Generation Software with Question Editor
for Windows® and Macintosh® Computers

Scott Foresman
Addison Wesley

Editorial Offices: Menlo Park, California • Glenview, Illinois • New York, New York
Sales Offices: Reading, Massachusetts • Atlanta, Georgia • Glenview, Illinois
Carrollton, Texas • Menlo Park, California

http://www.sf.aw.com

TestWorks™ is available on diskettes, in addition to CD-ROM, by special request. Call Scott Foresman - Addison Wesley Technical Support for details: 1-800-227-1936 or 1-800-982-6140 (within California).

Contents

Addison Wesley Longman License Agreement v

Introduction About TestWorks 1

Package Components 1

Hardware Requirements 2

Technical Support 2

Installation and Start-Up Before Installing 3

Installing the Program 3

Starting the Program 4

Setting the Password 5

Getting Help 6

Step-by-Step QuickStart 7

General Description Testbank Structure 10

of TestWorks Program Windows, Menus, and Buttons 10

Keyboard Shortcuts 15

Definition of Key Terms 16

Viewing and Modifying Opening a Testbank 17

Testbanks Using Outline View and Question View 17

Modifying the Testbank Display Format 19

Searching for Specific Questions 19

Modifying the Testbank 20

Creating and Modifying Tests Creating a New Test 22

Choosing a Sorting Method 22

Transferring Questions to a Test 24

Modifying or Adding Questions 26

Regenerating and Locking Variable Values 26

Scrambling Test Question Order 27

Modifying the Test Display and Format 27

Modifying Test Headers and Footers 29

Saving a Test 31

Opening an Existing Test 31

Using the Question Editor	Opening the Question Editor	**32**
	Multiple-Choice and Bimodal Questions	**33**
	True/False Questions	**34**
	Short-Answer and Essay Questions	**35**
	Matching Questions	**35**
	Typing and Aligning Text	**37**
	Using Special Symbols and Templates	**38**
	Defining, Inserting, and Viewing Variable	**39**
	Inserting Graphics	**41**
	Using the Graphing Tool	**43**
	Editing Instructions	**48**
	Editing Descriptors	**49**
	Saving Questions and Closing the Editor	**50**
Printing Tests and Testbanks	Choosing the Page Setup Options	**51**
	Setting the Test Print Options	**51**
	Setting the Testbank Print Options	**52**
Customizing TestWorks	Default Styles for Question Editor	**54**
	Fonts and Styles for Testbank Headings	**54**
	Regenerating Variables in a Testbank	**55**
	Resetting Field Values in a Testbank	**55**
	Sorting a Testbank	**55**
Creating a New Testbank	Testbank Setup	**57**
	Adding Titles and Questions	**59**
	Using the Spell Checker	**59**
Importing and Exporting Files	Importing Testbank Files	**60**
	Exporting Test Files	**63**
Technical Information & Troubleshooting		**64**
Appendix - Graphics Files		**65**
Limited Warranty		**68**
Correlations Between *Math Course 2* and Model Problems		**69**
Model Testbank Items		**81**

Addison Wesley Longman License Agreement

ADDISON WESLEY LONGMAN, INC. ("LICENSOR") IS WILLING TO LICENSE **TESTWORKS™ SOFTWARE** ("SOFTWARE") TO YOU ONLY IF YOU ACCEPT ALL OF THE TERMS IN THIS LICENSE AGREEMENT. PLEASE READ THE ENTIRE LICENSE AGREEMENT CAREFULLY BEFORE INSTALLING OR USING THE SOFTWARE, BECAUSE BY INSTALLING OR USING THE SOFT-WARE YOU ARE AGREEING TO BE BOUND BY THE TERMS OF THIS AGREE-MENT. IF YOU DO NOT AGREE TO THESE TERMS, LICENSOR WILL NOT LICENSE USE OF THE SOFTWARE TO YOU, AND IN THAT CASE YOU SHOULD TERMINATE THE INSTALLATION PROCESS AND RETURN THE SOFTWARE PROMPTLY, INCLUDING THE PACKAGING AND ALL WRITTEN MATERIALS, TO LICENSOR.

Ownership of Software

1. The Software fixed on this CD-ROM or on these diskettes in both Apple Macintosh® and Windows® operating systems and the accompanying written materials, if any, are owned by Licensor and are protected by U.S. copyright laws, by laws of other nations, and by international treaties. All rights not expressly granted to You in this Agreement are reserved by Licensor.

Grant of License

2. Licensor grants to You the non-exclusive right to use and display the Software and to copy the Software to any computers at a single school site and to the home computers of any teachers employed at that site, provided the Software is used only in conjunction with a developmental mathematics textbook published by Licensor ("Companion Textbook"). Licensor also grants to You a non-exclusive right to download and print out material from the Software, in whole or in part, provided the copies are distributed only to teachers and students in classes in which Licensor's Companion Textbook has been adopted for use. There will be no charge for this License, provided You are an adoptor of Licensor's Companion Textbook. If the Companion Textbook has not been adopted, You must secure a separate School Site License from Licensor, which will be subject to a flat fee and renewable on a yearly basis.

3. This License is valid for as long as You are an adoptor of Licensor's Companion Textbook. If You discontinue classroom use of the Companion Textbook and wish to continue using the Software or to copy material from the Software, You must contact Licensor to obtain a license specific to Your use. Failure to comply with these requirements will result in a clear violation of U.S. copyright laws. All other rights are reserved by Licensor.

Restrictions on Use

4. You may use the Software for non-profit educational purposes only.

5. You may not copy the Software in whole or in part, by any means whatsoever, for any purpose other than that stated above, without prior written permission from Licensor.

6. You may not display or transmit the Software in whole or in part on any type of wide area network system.

7. You may not modify, adapt, translate, or create derivative works based on the Software or on any accompanying written materials, except modifying or adding new testbank questions.

8. You may not reverse engineer, decompile, or disassemble the Software.

9. You may not sub-license, sell, lend, rent, or lease the Software or any copies created from the Software to any party, or derive any monetary compensation from use of the Software or from distribution of copies created from the Software.

Termination

10. If You fail to comply with any of the terms of the Agreement, Your right to use the Software will terminate automatically. No notice shall be required from Licensor to effect such termination. In the event of termination, You must cease using the Software and destroy all electronic and print copies of the Software in your possession. Failure to comply with these regulations upon termination of this Agreement will result in a clear violation of U.S. copyright law.

Limitations

11. Licensor makes no warranty, express or implied, with respect to the creation, distribution, or use of the Software or copies created from the Software.

12. IN NO EVENT WILL LICENSOR BE LIABLE TO YOU FOR DAMAGES, INCLUDING ANY LOSS OF PROFITS, LOST SAVINGS, OR OTHER INCIDENTAL OR CONSEQUENTIAL DAMAGES ARISING OUT OF YOUR USE OR INABILITY TO USE THE SOFTWARE. Because some states do not allow the exclusion or limitation of liability for consequential or incidental damages, the above limitation may not apply to You.

13. This Agreement is governed by the laws of the State of California.

14. If You have any questions concerning this Agreement or wish to contact Licensor for any reason, please write: Addison Wesley Longman, Inc., 2725 Sand Hill Road, Menlo Park, CA 94025.

0-201-31839-3

Introduction

ABOUT TESTWORKS

TestWorks is a test generator program that lets you view and edit testbank questions, transfer them to tests or practice sheets, and print in a variety of formats. The program also offers many options for organizing and displaying testbanks and tests. A built-in random number and text generator makes it ideal for creating multiple versions of tests by enabling variations on question models and by randomizing test item and multiple choices ordering. Powerful search and sort functions let you easily locate questions and arrange them in the order you prefer.

Features

The TestWorks software "engine" is used for many Scott Foresman - Addison Wesley software assessment products across several disciplines. The data for each textbook the software accompanies is what differs from product to product. The nature of the subject matter in various disciplines differs, so certain features below will be more useful for some subjects than for others. The following is a list of some of TestWorks' useful features.

- View testbanks and tests in outline form or question view
- Search for questions that meet your criteria
- Add or modify testbank questions using the editor
- Access online help and a glossary of terms
- Select test questions either manually or randomly
- Insert graphics in questions and store them in a graphics library
- Regenerate numbers or text in questions that allow variables
- Print up to twenty-five forms of a single test
- Automatically order test questions using built-in SmartSorts
- Clean up typos in a testbank or test using a built-in spell checker
- Use symbol palettes and expression templates to insert math notation and expressions
- Create Cartesian, polar, and number line graphs using a graphing tool
- Choose to display descriptor information for each question
- Choose from six question formats: multiple-choice, short-answer, true/false, matching, essay, and bimodal

PACKAGE COMPONENTS

Your TestWorks package includes:

- the TestWorks CD-ROM, from which the program files and chapter data files for your textbook will be installed to your hard disk;
- this TestWorks User's Guide.

HARDWARE REQUIREMENTS

Windows

TestWorks for Windows requires:

- microcomputer with a 486/50 or faster microprocessor;
- Windows 3.1 or Windows 95 operating system;
- minimum of 8 MB of available RAM (16 MB preferred);
- approximately 20 MB of hard disk space for installation;
- VGA color monitor and video driver;
- dot matrix graphics printer, inkjet, or laser printer with appropriate driver;
- mouse and a keyboard.

Macintosh

TestWorks for Macintosh requires:

- 68030 or later, or PowerMac cpu;
- System 7.0 or later operating system;
- minimum 8 MB of available RAM;
- minimum 20 MB of hard disk space for installation;
- color monitor and video driver;
- inkjet or laser printer with appropriate driver;
- mouse and a keyboard.

TECHNICAL SUPPORT

For immediate answers to commonly asked technical support questions, see the Scott Foresman - Addison Wesley FAQ (frequently asked questions) site at http://www.sf.aw.com/techsupport/

Technical support for TestWorks is also available through the Scott Foresman - Addison Wesley Technical Support line: 1-800-227-1936 or 1-800-982-6140 (within California).

TestWorks is available on diskettes, in addition to CD-ROM, by special request to Technical Support.

Installation and Start-Up

This section covers the steps for installing and starting the TestWorks program for Windows and Macintosh computers. It also describes TestWorks' online help.

Instructions are provided for installation from a CD (standard) or from diskettes (special order). Diskette installation alternatives will typically appear in parentheses.

BEFORE INSTALLING

Before installing the program, place the TestWorks CD (or Program Disk 1) in the appropriate drive. If there is a README file, open it to read important information about changes in the TestWorks installation or program operation.

INSTALLING THE PROGRAM

If you are installing from diskettes instead of from the standard CD, separate the disks into Program disks and Testbank disks, then follow the instructions below for the type of computer you have. You may want to make backups of the disks before using them to install the program. Make sure the disks remain locked during installation.

Windows 3.1 or Windows 95

Place the CD (or Program Disk 1) in the appropriate drive and choose Run on the File menu (Windows 3.1) or Start menu (Windows 95) to run D:\SETUP. (If necessary, replace "D" with the appropriate letter of the CD or diskette drive from which you are installing.) If you want to use File Manager or Windows Explorer, locate SETUP.EXE on the CD (or diskette) and double-click it to launch the installation program.

When the Welcome to TestWorks Installation menu appears, choose from one of the following menu choices:

1. *Install TestWorks Program and Testbank Files*
   This option allows you to install all the files necessary to run TestWorks and also installs the testbank included with the program as well as graphic files. If TestWorks has already been installed for a different textbook, do not use this installation option. Instead, use option 3 below to install the new testbank only.

2. *Install TestWorks Program Files Only*
   This option allows you to install only the program files for TestWorks. Use this option for upgrades and updates.

3. *Install Testbank Files Only*
   This option allows you to install a testbank without installing the TestWorks program files. Use this option if TestWorks has already been installed and you are installing additional testbanks.

4. *Exit Without Installing*
   This option allows you to exit the installation program and return to Windows.

The default pathname for installation is C:\TESTWRKS, but you can specify a different drive and directory if desired. Testbank files do not have to be installed in the same directory as the program.

Follow the instructions on the screen to install the TestWorks program, one or more books of testbank questions, and a folder containing graphic files.

Macintosh

(NOTE: If you have a disk virus scanner running, restart your Macintosh with Extensions off before doing this installation. Do so by holding down the SHIFT *key when you restart the computer.)*

Insert the CD-ROM (or Program Disk 1) in the appropriate drive. If necessary, double-click the disk icon to open its window. Double-click the TestWorks Installer icon, then follow the instructions on the screen to install the TestWorks program. You can indicate the disk (except the CD) or folder where you want to install the TestWorks folder. When installation is complete, you can rename the TestWorks folder, but do not rename any of the program files contained in the folder.

Choose from one of the following menu choices:

1. *Install TestWorks Program and Testbank Files*
   This option allows you to install all the files necessary to run TestWorks and also installs the testbank included with the program as well as graphic files. If TestWorks has already been installed for a different subject matter, do not use this installation option. Instead, use option 3 below to install the new testbank only.

2. *Install TestWorks Program Files Only*
   This option allows you to install only the program files for TestWorks. Use this option for upgrades and updates.

3. *Install Testbank Files Only*
   This option allows you to install a testbank without installing the TestWorks program files. Use this option if TestWorks has already been installed and you are installing additional testbanks. Testbank files do not have to be installed in the same folder as the program.

STARTING THE PROGRAM

(IMPORTANT: After installation is complete, the CD (or installation diskettes) may be kept in a safe place. The program runs entirely from your hard disk.)

To start the TestWorks program, follow these instructions for your computer.

Windows 3.1

Double-click the TestWorks icon in the Program Manager. If you do not see a TestWorks icon, launch the File Manager. Open the TESTWRKS folder on your hard disk or the alternate folder to which TestWorks was installed. Double-click the TESTWRKS.EXE file to start the program. You will first see the title screen, then the password registration screen.

Windows 95

Choose TestWorks on the Programs menu. If the TestWorks program is not on your Programs menu, run Windows Explorer or open My Computer and locate the TESTWRKS folder on your hard disk or the alternate folder to which TestWorks was installed. Double-click the TESTWRKS.EXE application to start the program. *(NOTE: The .EXE extension may not appear.)*

If graphics or text appear truncated, set your display resolution to 640 x 480, or change the display setting from Large Fonts to Small Fonts. If you plan to print to a non-PostScript™ printer, use your Windows 95 Printers Setting to set the Spool Data Format to RAW. For details, see the "Technical Information & Troubleshooting" section.

Macintosh

Open the TestWorks folder on your hard disk or the alternate folder to which TestWorks was installed. Double-click the TestWorks application file to start the program.

SETTING THE PASSWORD

The first time you use the TestWorks program, you may choose a password to be used each time you start the program. This will prevent unauthorized users from running the program and getting access to the testbank questions and your test files. To set a password, type up to eight characters in the space provided, then click the OK button. If you do not want to use a password, click the No Password button.

Your password is saved with the program and cannot be retrieved in any way once you have entered it, so if you happen to forget your password, you will not be able to start the program. In this case, if you have the Windows version of the program, you will need to delete the user preferences file "userpref.prf" from the directory containing the TestWorks program files. If you have the Macintosh version, delete the file "TGEQ Prefs." Then, restart the program and register a new password. *(NOTE: If you delete the user preferences file, you will lose other settings you may have chosen.)*

If you are concerned about security, keep your password secret or stored in a safe place. Also keep the TestWorks CD (or diskettes) in a secure place.

GETTING HELP

TestWorks has a built-in Help function you can access from the Help menu. When you choose Help you can locate the information you need by using either the Contents button or the Glossary button.

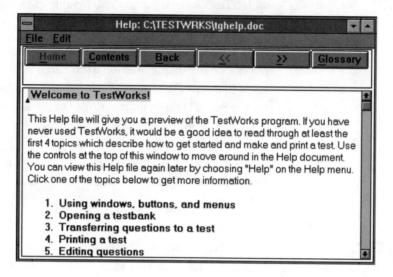

Table of Contents

The Contents button will display the table of contents for the Help document. When you click on a topic in the Table of Contents and then click the Go To button, you will see a window that displays information about that topic. You can also click the blue, underlined words in the Help window to get information or to go to another location in the Help file.

To move from one topic to the next, click the Forward button [>>]; to go to the previous topic, click the Back button [<<]. The Home button will take you to the initial Help screen.

Glossary of Terms

The Glossary button will display an alphabetical list of terms that pertain to TestWorks. Use the scroll bar to find the term you want. Then, click and hold on the term to read the definition in a pop-up box.

Step-by-Step QuickStart

This section will give you a quick introduction to the basic process of building a test with TestWorks. In this Quickstart, users are asked to use menu choices to perform actions. For more information on the equivalent screen buttons for these actions, see the "General Description of TestWorks" section of this Guide.

To get familiar with TestWorks, start the program as described in "Installation and Start-Up." Explore the online Help topics that appear at launch, then exit Help by clicking (double-clicking in Windows) the close box in the upper left corner of the Help window. Now follow the general directions below to build and print a test. For more detailed instructions or information about additional features, refer to later parts of this Guide.

STEP 1.
OPEN A TESTBANK

On the File menu of the Main window, choose Open Book and locate a book file in the file dialog window. Book files are named with short descriptive titles associated with their subject matters and have a **.BOK** extension. When you open the book file, the testbank will be in Outline view and you will see a list of the chapters in the testbank in the Book window.

STEP 2.
START A NEW TEST

Next, choose New Test on the File menu of the Main window and name the test. Windows users must limit the name to eight characters with no spaces. The test name will automatically be appended with the extension **.TST** so that it will be easy to find in the future. After you name the test, you will see the Test window with no questions in it. You will create a test by transferring questions from the book, or testbank.

STEP 3.
VIEW THE TESTBANK

To begin choosing questions for a chapter test, click on the Book window to make it the active window (its title bar will turn dark for Windows or gray on Macintosh). Click once on the small arrow at the left of one of the chapter titles to open the chapter and display the section titles or question types. Click on the arrow to the left of the first section or question type to display another level, and so on. Since you are in Outline view, under the lowest level of titles, you will see a reference for each question in the testbank. Below the question will be some descriptive information, the question type, and the number of variations that the question may have.

If you want to view the questions themselves, click Question View on the View menu. One section at a time will be visible in this mode. To navigate to other sections, choose Next Question Group or Previous Question Group from the Navigate menu. You may need to use the scroll bar to view more questions within a section.

STEP 4.
TRANSFER
QUESTIONS
MANUALLY

To transfer questions manually to a test, you can be in either Outline view or Question view. Let's start with picking one question and transferring it to the test. Click on a testbank item to select it (it will highlight). Now choose Transfer After in the Tools menu. The question will be copied and become the first question on your test. Notice that the target at the top of the Test window has an arrow in it, so it is the "target" for transferred questions.

If the testbank questions contain variables for randomized numbers or text, you can transfer multiple copies of a single question. Locate and click to select a question whose variations descriptor, Var: #, indicates that there is more than one variation of the item. (Some subject matters, especially mathematics, offer more opportunities to include these "dynamic" questions than others. If your subject has fewer, you may need to navigate to locate one.) Type a number, such as 2, in the Quantity box at the top of the Book window. Choose Transfer After (or Transfer Before, if it is visible) from the Tools menu, and multiple copies of the question will be transferred to the test, each with different numbers or text, depending on the assigned variables.

You can also select more than one question and then transfer all the selected questions at once. To make multiple selections, hold down the SHIFT key when you click the mouse to select a question.

If you make multiple selections of a question containing variables and enter a number in the Quantity box, you will get multiple copies of each selected question when you transfer them.

A bimodal question (denoted Type: BI) is a multiple-choice question that may also be used as a short-answer question. Locate at least one and transfer it to your test.

STEP 5.
TRANSFER
QUESTIONS
RANDOMLY

To have the computer choose questions randomly for a test, switch to Outline view and select the title of the chapter, section, or problem type from which you want to choose questions. Do *not* select an individual test item or question reference. Enter the number of questions you want to transfer in the Quantity box at the top of the Book window. Choose Transfer from the Tools menu, then, if necessary, reset the Quantity box entry to 1.

You may also select more than one heading at the same level. The number you type in the Quantity box will determine the number of questions that will be randomly chosen from *each* section you have selected.

STEP 6.
MODIFY TEST
HEADERS AND
FORMAT

After you have made all the question selections you want for the test, click in the Test window to make it the active window. You can change the way a test is displayed and printed by choosing these options on the Setup menu: Page Headers, Question Type Headers, Format, and Display. Each of the Setup options is described in more detail later in this Guide. For this sample test, choose Page Headers and edit the headers and footers that will appear on each page. Click (double-click in Windows) the close box in the window's upper left corner when you are finished.

STEP 7.
PRINT THE TEST

Click the Test window to make it active. Make sure it is in Question view. In Question view, the features of your printed test are visible, so manipulating the Test window display also determines the format of what is printed. Choose Print on the File menu. Enter 2 for the Number of Forms. Be sure there is an X in the check box next to Print Answer Key. Click OK. When the system print dialog appears, make sure All in the print range is selected and click OK to print your test. On the two versions of your printed test, notice that the question order and choices within multiple-choice items have been varied. Also, the variable parts of dynamic items (those with a variations number of more than one) are different.

Now, with the Test window still active, choose Display from the Tools menu. Click to put an X in the box labeled Print Bimodal Questions as Short Answer, then click OK. Notice that the bimodal questions in the Test window now appear as short-answer questions instead of multiple-choice. The form of bimodal questions can also be changed individually. Choose Print again from the File menu. Print two versions again, but this time click to choose the Preserve Question Order option, and click OK. Notice that the order of questions in both versions of the new test are the same.

STEP 8.
QUIT

From the File menu, choose Exit (Quit on Macintosh). Your currently open test will be saved automatically.

General Description of TestWorks

This section gives a general description of the structure, windows, and buttons used in TestWorks.

TESTBANK STRUCTURE The TestWorks software "engine" is used for many Scott Foresman - Addison Wesley software assessment products across several disciplines. The data for each textbook the software accompanies is what differs from product to product. The organizational structure of your textbook has been adapted to a standard testbank structure used in all TestWorks products. Throughout this guide, *Chapter* is used to refer to the highest level of organization, and *section* and *subsection* refer to sublevels of organization under chapter. Each chapter and section title in the testbank will include the title of that level in your textbook.

PROGRAM WINDOWS, MENUS, AND BUTTONS

Main Window and Status Bar

After starting the program and entering your password, you will see the Main Program window for TestWorks. It contains all the menus for the program along with commonly used editing, navigation, and format buttons and a status bar.

When you move the mouse pointer across any of the active buttons in the Main window, the Book window, or the Test window, the status bar gives a description of the button.

Main Window Buttons The first eight buttons in the Main window are commonly used for editing text. You may also use the Edit menu to perform these functions on the Book window or the Test window, whichever is currently active.

  Add Add an object of the same type (chapter, section, question, etc.) as what is selected, before or after selected item, depending on the setting of the State button. This option does not add items to a test. Instead, it enables the user to create new chapters, sections, or testbank items.

  Delete Delete one or more selected questions. When a header is deleted, all the questions under the header are deleted.

  Modify Edit a selected question or heading.

Cut   Delete the selected questions or headers. When a header is cut, all the questions under the header are cut. Cut questions remain in memory. See Insert and Replace below.

 Copy   Copy the selected questions or headers. When headers are copied, all the questions under the header are copied into memory.

 State   Toggle the add, insert, and transfer states between Before and After. Ignored in tests with a SmartSort on.

 Insert   Insert a previously copied or cut like item before or after the selected item. Headers cannot be inserted while in Question view.

 Replace   Replace the selected like item with a previously cut or copied item.

The five buttons to the right of the editing buttons are commonly used to navigate and display questions in a testbank or test, whichever is the active window. Options in the Navigate menu may also be used to perform these functions.

 Previous   Display previous section of a testbank or page of a test.

 Next   Display next section of a testbank or page of a test.

 Jump   Display a specific chapter of a testbank or page of a test.

 First   Display the first section of a testbank or page of a test.

 Last   Display the last section of a testbank or page of a test.

The two rightmost buttons in the button bar of the Main window are used to alter the display or contents of a testbank or test.

 Setup   Set up format of text components of a testbank or test. This function is also available as the Format option in the Setup menu.

 Reset   Reset values for specific fields in a testbank. This function is also available as the Global Field Reset option in the Setup menu.

Book Window

The Book window, which displays the testbank questions, opens when you choose Open Book or New Book from the File menu. Initially, the testbank questions are displayed in Outline view, which lets you see how questions are organized for each chapter. Question references for each chapter and sub-section can be revealed by single-clicking the small display arrows located to the left of each header in the outline.

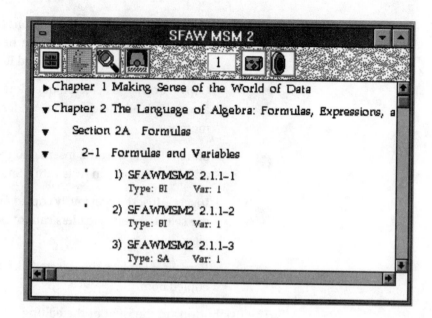

In Outline view, each question reference is a unique label containing a book ID, a multipart number that indicates the question's relative position in the book, and the question number. You can view the questions by changing the viewing mode of the testbank from Outline view to Question view using the first button in the Book window.

Book Window Buttons   The buttons in the Book window are used to manipulate the testbank questions, change the way they are displayed, and to transfer questions to a test.

 Mode   Changes the display mode for the Book window, toggling between Outline view and Question view. These functions are also available in the View menu.

 Regenerate   Generates a new set of values for all the variables included in the selected questions. This function is also available in the Tools menu when the Book window is active.

 Search   Displays a subset of the questions in the testbank that match a user-defined search criteria. This function is also available in the Tools menu.

 Display   Lets you decide which descriptors should be displayed with each question in the testbank. This function is also available in the Setup menu.

 Transfer   Copies single or multiple copies of manually or randomly selected questions to the Target window, usually the test. To the left of the Transfer button is the Quantity box where you can enter the number of copies of manually selected or randomly selected questions you would like to transfer to a test. This function is also available in the Tools menu.

 Target   Selects or deselects the window as a target for questions that are transferred from other windows. This function is also available in the Setup menu.

Test Window

The Test window opens when you choose Open Test or New Test from the File menu. The Test window displays test questions in Outline or Question view and contains buttons that are most commonly needed to manipulate the test questions.

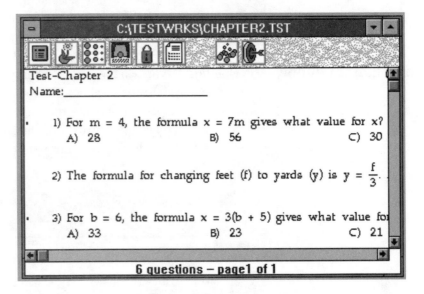

Initially, the test questions are displayed in Question view, which lets you see the pages of a test exactly as they will be printed. You can also view a test in Outline view, where just a reference to each question is listed and you can see how the questions are grouped or organized.

Test Window Buttons The picture buttons in the Test window are used to manipulate test questions and to change the way they are displayed.

 Mode Changes the display mode for the test, toggling between Outline view and Question view. These functions can be performed from the View menu when the Test window is active.

 Regenerate Generates a new set of values for all the variables in the selected questions. This function can be performed from the Tools menu when the Test window is active.

 Sort Puts the test questions in order according to a preprogrammed or Custom SmartSort or a User-Defined Order. This function can be performed from the Tools menu when the Test window is active.

 Display Lets you decide which descriptors should be displayed with each question on the test. This function can be performed from the Setup menu when the Test window is active.

 Lock Locks the values for selected questions that contain variable numbers or text. This function is also available in the Tools menu.

 Form Switches the form of a bimodal question (multiple-choice or short-answer) to the opposite of the global setting. This function is also available in the Tools menu.

Scramble Changes the order of the questions on a test, while still maintaining the rules of the current sort criteria. This function is also available in the Tools menu.

 Target Selects or deselects the window as a target for questions that are transferred from other windows. This function can be performed from the Setup menu when the Test window is active.

Question Editor Window

The Question Editor window opens when you choose to add or modify a question in a testbank or on a test. The look of the Question Editor window varies slightly, depending on the question type. In general, the Question Editor window shows the Instruction, Question, and Answer fields for the question. Additional descriptive information, such as a page reference, may also be included.

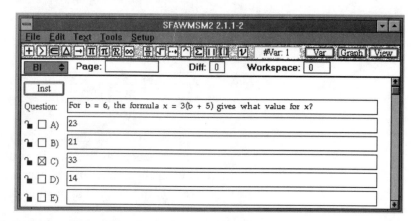

The Question Editor window also contains buttons and menu items that let you define regenerating variables, insert special symbols or math templates, import graphics, or plot mathematical graphs. Every Editor window has the standard components described below.

Symbol Palettes and Expression Templates Buttons at the top of each Question Editor window help you enter special symbols that cannot be typed from the keyboard and mathematical expressions or tables that require special formatting. The symbol bar includes nine palettes of symbols and seven palettes of templates.

Variables The v button lets you insert variable numbers or text in any question, indicated by a V and a number. The Var button leads to the Variable Definitions Worksheet where the number or text values for each variable are defined. When variables are used in a question, the #Var field automatically calculates and displays the number of possible variations.

The View button allows you to display either the variable names or the variable values in the Editor window. More information about using variables in your test questions is given in the "Defining, Inserting and Viewing Variables" subsection of this Guide.

The Graph Button   The Graph button leads to a built-in graphing tool where you can create mathematical graphs on Cartesian, polar, or number line coordinate systems. The graphs can then be inserted into any part of a question. This function is also available as the Create Graph option in the Tools menu. More information about using the graphing tool is given in the "Using the Graph Tool" subsection of this Guide.

Ruler   A ruler may be displayed if you want to set tabs, text justification, or margins for selected parts of a question. More details about how to use the ruler are given in the "Typing and Aligning Text" subsection of this Guide.

Input Fields   A number of areas in the Editor window allow you to enter information for multiple-choice, short-answer, true/false, matching, essay, and bimodal question types. In addition to entering the question and answer, you can enter a page reference, difficulty level, amount of workspace and other descriptive information. The process of choosing question types and entering questions is described in the "Using the Question Editor" section of this Guide.

KEYBOARD SHORTCUTS

Many of the options that are on the TestWorks menus and buttons can also be performed by using a keyboard shortcut specific to the type of computer you are using.

Windows Version

Pull-down menus on an active window can be displayed by using the ALT key (Windows) or the OPTION key (Macintosh) in combination with the underlined letter in the menu name. Once a menu is displayed, activate any option by typing its underlined letter. For example, to view a testbank in Question view, display the View menu by pressing ALT-V. Next, type **Q** since it is the underlined letter for that menu item. Press the ESC key to close the menu.

In the Windows version, you may use F1 to access Help and ALT-F4 to exit the program.

Windows and Macintosh Versions

The following letters, in combination with the CTRL key (Windows) or the command key ⌘ (Macintosh), perform these menu functions.

A	Add	**O**	Open Test
B	Bold	**P**	Print
C	Copy	**Q**	Quit (Mac only)
D	Delete	**R**	Regenerate
E	Expand Level	**S**	Save As
G	Graph	**T**	Transfer
I	Italic	**U**	Underline
J	Jump	**V**	Insert
K	Collapse All	**W**	Close/Save Changes
L	Spell	**X**	Cut
M	Modify	**Z**	Undo
N	New Test		

DEFINITION OF KEY TERMS

Active window   The window currently selected as evidenced by a title bar that is the same color as the Main Program window.

Bimodal questions   Questions that are displayed in multiple-choice format in a testbank, but can be displayed in either multiple-choice or short-answer format on a test.

Book file   A file that contains all the questions in a testbank. The book file name ends in **.BOK.**

Book window   A window that displays all the questions in a testbank.

Descriptors   Information assigned to each question in order to classify it or describe it (e.g., page reference).

Graphing tool   A tool that lets you create mathematical graphs on Cartesian, polar, or number line axes.

Manual selection   Choose specific questions to transfer to a test.

Outline view   The view of a testbank or a test that lets you see how the questions are grouped or organized.

Question editor   A tool that opens when you add a new question or modify a question in a testbank or a test.

Question reference   A unique label assigned to each question that includes the book ID, the question's relative position in the book, and the question number.

Question view   The view of a testbank or a test that lets you see the text of each question.

Random selection   Choose a number of questions randomly from a selected chapter, section, or question type.

Regenerate   Have the computer randomly choose new number values or text strings for questions containing variables.

Scramble   Change the order of the questions on a test to produce a new form of the test.

Search   Locate and display only those questions in a testbank that match the criteria defined by the user.

Shuffle   Change the order of the answer choices for multiple-choice or bimodal questions to produce a new form of a question.

Sort   Group the questions on a test according to question type or other sort criteria.

Target window   The window selected as the target for questions being transferred.

Test window   A window that displays all the questions selected for a test.

Viewing and Modifying Testbanks

This section discusses how to open a testbank and work with it in order to select questions for a test. See the "General Description of TestWorks" section of this Guide for more details on the buttons and menu choices that follow.

OPENING A TESTBANK

To open a testbank, start the TestWorks program and choose Open Book from the File menu. When the file dialog appears, you will need to locate a book file. The book file will usually be named with an abbreviation for the textbook and will end in the extension .BOK. You might see, for example, SFAWMSM2.BOK or SFAWM3.BOK. If the book file was not installed in the same directory or folder as the TestWorks program, you will need to change to a different directory or folder to locate the book file. Select the book you want and click OK or Open.

USING OUTLINE VIEW AND QUESTION VIEW

A testbank can be viewed in two different viewing modes—Outline view and Question view. Outline view lets you get an overall picture of how the testbank is organized and move easily from one part to another. In Outline view, you can see question references, but not the actual questions. Question view lets you view the actual questions for any of the lowest levels. You can easily switch between the two modes by clicking the Mode button or by choosing either of the two modes on the View menu.

Outline View

The book will open automatically in Outline view so that you can see the list of chapter titles. The arrows to the left of each title are used to display the contents of each chapter. Click once on an arrow to see what is contained in the chapter. If there are sections within a chapter, they can also be opened by clicking on an arrow to display more of the contents of the chapter.

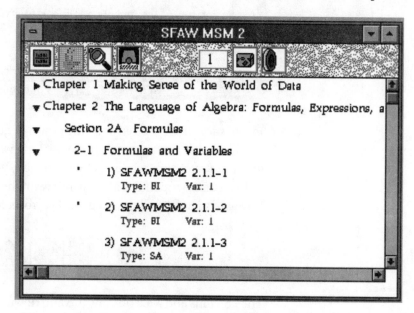

When you have opened a chapter to its lowest level, you will see a reference for each question. The question reference includes a book ID, a multipart number that indicates the question's relative position in the book, and the question number. For example, the question reference SFAWMth2 2.1.1-1

indicates that this is question 1 from chapter 2, first section, first lesson of the book abbreviated as SFAWMth2. The first section may be a physical section of the textbook or whatever is the second level of organization of the testbank.

If you would like to view all of the questions in a specific chapter, section, or subsection, click on its title to select it. Then choose Expand Level on the View menu of the Main window. All sublevel headers will expand to reveal the question references in each. To close the subheadings in a testbank and display only the chapter titles, choose Collapse All on the View menu.

You may also use the scroll bar in the Book window to move around while in Outline view. Click repeatedly on the up or down arrows or drag the slider.

Question View

Choose Question view when you want to see the questions and answers for any section of a chapter. The questions will be displayed in a scrolling window and be identified by a number. There may or may not be descriptive information shown with each question, depending on your choice of display format and the testbank contents.

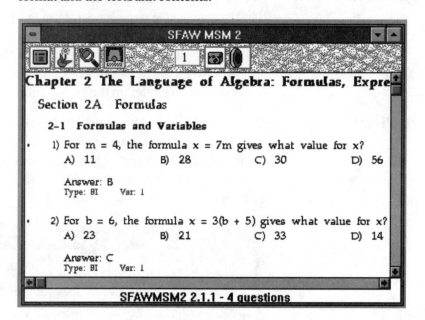

In Question view, you see only one group of questions at a time and you can use the scroll bar to see all the questions within that group. To see other groups of questions while in Question view, you need to use the navigation buttons at the top of the Main window or choose related commands on the Navigate menu. The buttons include arrows for Previous, Next, Jump, First, and Last.

The Previous and Next buttons (up and down arrows) take you up or down in the outline to the previous or next group of questions. The Jump button (curved arrow) lets you choose a chapter and then displays the first set of questions from that chapter. The First button (up arrow with a bar) takes you to the first group of questions in the testbank. The Last button (down arrow with a bar) takes you to the last group of questions in the testbank.

MODIFYING THE TESTBANK DISPLAY FORMAT

See the "General Description of TestWorks" section of this Guide for more details on the buttons and menu choices that follow.

Descriptive information, such as topic, difficulty level, or page reference may be assigned to the questions in a testbank. Usually some, but not all, descriptive information is provided in the program for any specific textbook. Other descriptive information may be entered by the user. Whether you are in Outline view or Question view, you can decide which descriptive information you want to be displayed to help you decide which questions to use for a test. If the testbank you are using does not contain such descriptive information, you may want to enter it yourself or turn off all the display options.

To make these choices, click the Display button at the top of the Book window or choose Display from the Setup menu while the Book window is active. You will see the Testbank Display Options dialog.

Clicking in the check box next to any of the options will change the display of the testbank so that the checked items are shown below each question reference or question after you click OK.

SEARCHING FOR SPECIFIC QUESTIONS

See the "General Description of TestWorks" section of this Guide for more details on the buttons and menu choices that follow.

One way to locate questions for a test is to search the testbank for questions that meet a certain criteria. For example, you might want to view only those questions that have a difficulty level of 2, or are multiple-choice questions, or have some combination of attributes. (NOTE: Usually some, but not all, descriptive information is provided in the program for any specific textbook. Other descriptive information may be entered by the user.)

In the Book window, click the Search button or choose Search on the Tools menu to display the Testbank Search Criteria dialog.

Change the settings for any category by choosing from the pull-down menus in Columns 2 and 3. The combination of all the settings will define the set of questions you will see when you click the radio button for Show Only Questions That Meet Criteria Above.

When you return to the Book window, it is possible that none of the questions in certain sections will match the search criteria you defined. In this case, only the level headings will be visible; questions that do not match the search criteria will not be visible. In Outline view, choose Expand Level to see the selected question references. In Question view, click the navigation buttons until you get to a section where questions match the criteria.

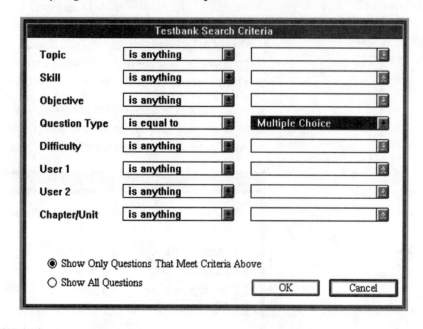

MODIFYING THE TESTBANK

You are able to modify a testbank by editing the chapter or section titles, editing individual questions, and also by adding new questions, sections, or chapters. See the "General Description of TestWorks" section of this Guide for more details on the buttons and menu choices that follow.

Editing Titles

To modify any of the titles in the testbank, double-click the title you want to change. This will open a small editing window where you can change the text.

Click OK when you are done editing the title or Cancel to exit without changes.

To change the font or style of the titles in the testbank, use the Format command on the Setup menu. The Testbank Setup dialog box is explained in the "Customizing TestWorks" section of this Guide.

Modifying Questions

You can edit any question in the testbank by double-clicking on any part of the question in Outline or Question view. You can also click once on the question and then click on the Modify button in the Main window. This will display the Question Editor window where all the parts of the question will be shown along with any descriptive information. (Choose Show Descriptors from the Tools menu if the descriptors are not visible beneath the question and you want to edit this information.) The process of editing questions is described in more detail in the "Using the Question Editor" chapter of this Guide.

Adding Questions

You can add your own new questions to any section of the testbank. Go to the part of the testbank where you want to add a question. Select a question by first clicking on it, then clicking the Add button or choosing Add (After or Before) from the Edit menu. A new question will be added After or Before the selected question, depending on the setting of the State button in the Main window. (The State button will show either an object following three dots if the current state is After or an object preceding three dots if the current state is Before.) You can change the setting of the State button by clicking on it or by choosing Change After to Before or Change Before to After on the Edit menu.

When you select a question, then choose Add, the Question Editor window will open. Choose a question type from the pull-down menu and begin entering your question and answer. More details about using the Question Editor are given in the "Using the Question Editor" chapter of this Guide.

Adding Chapters and Sections

You can add new chapters or sections to any part of the testbank. In Outline view, go to the part of the testbank where you want to add a chapter or section. If you want to add a chapter of new questions, click once on a chapter title to select it. If you want to add a new section, click once on a section title to select it. Your new chapter or section will be added after or before the selected chapter or section depending on the setting of the State button.

When you select a chapter or section title, then choose Add from the Edit menu, the program will insert a dummy chapter or section title before or after the selected chapter or section. It will also insert dummy titles for all the levels below the level you selected and one dummy question at the lowest level.

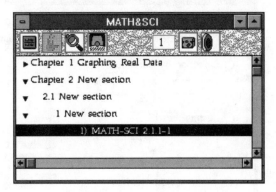

You will need to edit each title to reflect its intended content and edit the dummy question by entering its question, answer, etc. You can then continue to add new questions or sections as needed to complete the chapter. More details about using the Question Editor are given in the "Using the Question Editor" chapter of this Guide.

Creating and Modifying Tests

This section discusses how to create a new test and modify an existing test. Topics include transferring testbank questions, modifying and adding questions, modifying headers and footers, and modifying test format and display.

See the "General Description of TestWorks" section of this Guide for more details on the buttons and menu choices that follow.

CREATING A NEW TEST

To create a new test, first open a book, or testbank, from which you will choose questions. Then choose New Test from the File menu. A window will open where you can name the test. A .TST extension will be automatically added to the name you assign (on Macintosh, you may opt to add the .TST extension, or not). A Test window will open and you will see the current main header for the test. The test is ready to receive questions that you transfer from the Book window, but before you start choosing questions, you may want to choose a sorting method for the test.

CHOOSING A SORTING METHOD

TestWorks provides you with a set of predefined sorting methods called SmartSorts so that when you transfer questions to a test, the questions will be grouped or arranged in a specific order. To use a SmartSort, be sure the Test window is active, then click on the Sort button or choose Sort from the Tools menu.

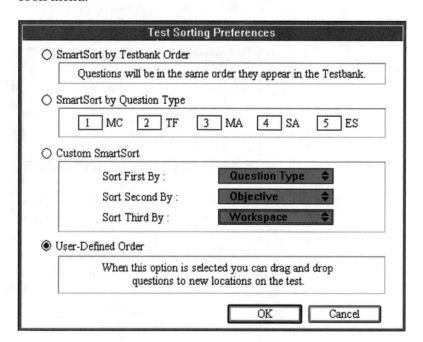

You can choose one of the predefined SmartSorts, create your own Custom SmartSort, or turn sorting off by using a User-Defined Order. You can switch between SmartSorts at any time, or switch to a User-Defined Order after using a SmartSort.

(CAUTION: If you switch from User-Defined Order to a SmartSort, the program does not remember your User-Defined Order.)

Sort by Testbank Order

When you sort by Testbank Order, the questions on your test will be ordered according to the levels of organization used in the testbank. For example, the questions may be ordered by chapter, section, and question number.

Sort by Question Type

When you choose to sort by Question Type, the questions on your test will be put in order according to the types of questions used in the testbank; for example, Short Answer, Multiple Choice, and Essay. You can specify the order of the question types by assigning each a number. The program will automatically supply a question type header before each question type. For information on how to edit question type headers, refer to the "Modifying Test Headers and Footers" section of this Guide.

Custom SmartSort

When you choose a Custom SmartSort, you can specify up to three levels of sorting for a test. Use the pull-down menus on the sort dialog box to set up the sort criteria. For example, you can arrange to sort questions first by question type, then by chapter, and then by difficulty level. You do not need to specify all 3 levels. Any time you specify question type as one of the sort levels, the program will supply a question type header for each question type you include. For information on how to edit question type headers, see the "Modifying Test Headers and Footers" section of this Guide.

User-Defined Order

When you choose to use a User-Defined Order for a test, you can choose the exact order for the test questions. The program will not perform any SmartSort. As the simplest example, if the State button is set to After, questions will appear on the test in the order they are transferred.

Arranging Questions In either Outline view or Question view on a test, you can rearrange the questions by simply dragging them from one location to another. In the Macintosh version of TestWorks, select the question and drag it while holding down the mouse button. In the Windows version, drag while holding down the *right* mouse button. Drop the question into place by releasing the mouse button. For example, if you want to move the first question on the test to be the third question, select the first question, then drag until the icon is anywhere in the area of the third question, then drop the question. You can also perform cut-and-paste operations to move one or more questions at a time. The program will not group questions in any way if you have selected the User-Defined Order option.

Adding Notes When User-Defined Order is chosen, you may want to insert headings or other instructions on your test. Select a question you want to have preceded by a note and choose Note List on the Edit menu. This will open up the Note List where you can choose a note, edit a note, or add new notes to the list. Clicking Edit or Add brings up the User Note Editor. The note you choose will become part of the question and can be shared by several questions, just like an instruction.

Switching Between Sort Methods

It is possible to switch from one SmartSort to another and back again without disastrous results. However, sometimes switching between a SmartSort and User-Defined Order will produce results that are confusing if you are unaware of the following distinctions.

SmartSort to SmartSort   When you switch from one SmartSort to another after you have selected questions for a test, the questions will simply be reorganized according to the rules of the new SmartSort.

SmartSort to User-Defined Order   When you switch from a SmartSort to User-Defined Order after choosing questions for a test, all the SmartSort rules for grouping questions are abandoned and the test becomes a list of questions that you can rearrange in any order. Initially, the order of the questions on a User-Defined test converted from a SmartSort will be exactly the same as on the SmartSort test. If you add any new questions after converting to a User-Defined Order, they will be inserted where you want them and not placed in any predetermined order by the program. You can add Notes to questions as needed.

User-Defined Order to SmartSort   When you switch from a User-Defined Order to a SmartSort after choosing questions for a test, the questions will be regrouped according to the SmartSort rules and the new SmartSort will insert its own question type headings as needed. Your User-Defined Order will not be remembered by the program, so there is no Undo option to go back once the SmartSort is selected. You may want to clear any Notes from your questions.

TRANSFERRING QUESTIONS TO A TEST

TestWorks gives you many ways to transfer copies of testbank questions to a test.

Setting the Target Window

When you create a New Test, the Test window automatically becomes the target window and displays an arrow in the Target button in the upper right corner of the window. This means that it will be the target for any questions you transfer from a testbank to the test. If you have more than one Test window open at the same time, only one of these windows can be the Target window. You can set a window as a Target window by clicking the Target button in the upper right corner of the window or by choosing Set As Target on the Setup menu.

Using the Transfer Button and Quantity Box

The Transfer button at the top of the Book window is used to transfer copies of the selected question(s) to the Target window. The Quantity box, which is a small input window to the left of the Transfer button, lets you type a number to transfer multiple copies of selected questions or to choose a number of questions randomly from a selected section.

Selecting Questions Manually

Single Question   To select a single question and transfer it to a test, click once on the question in either Outline view or Question view and then click the Transfer button. A copy of the question will be moved to the Target window. You may also manually drag the question from the book to the test by selecting the question and holding down the mouse button (Macintosh) or the *right* mouse button (Windows) and then drop it in place by releasing the mouse.

If a SmartSort is turned on, the question will move to the correct location according to the rules of the SmartSort. If you are creating a test in User-Defined Order, the question will be inserted before or after the question selected in the Test window, depending on the setting of the State button.

Multiple Questions   To select more than one question in the book, click on a single question to select it. Then hold down the SHIFT key and click on one or more additional questions. Finally, click the Transfer button to copy the questions to the Target window.

Multiple Copies of a Single Question   If the testbank contains questions that include variable numbers or text, such as in a testbank for a math book, you can copy different randomly generated variations of a single question to a test. Select a question in the testbank and enter the number of variations you want in the Quantity box. Then click the Transfer button and the number of questions you selected will be transferred to the test. Each variation should include different randomly generated numbers or text strings.

Note that one of the descriptors for each question in a testbank is the number of variations it may assume, or #Var. Each variation is formed by replacing variable parts in the model question with a number or text from a defined replacement set.

(NOTE: If no variables are used in a test question, #Var will have a value of 1, and trying to transfer multiple copies of the question will result in a warning message asking you if you want to allow duplicate questions on your test.)

Multiple Copies of Multiple Questions   If a testbank contains questions that include variable numbers or text, you can make multiple selections and then request multiple copies of each question selected. First select the questions you want while holding the SHIFT key, then enter a number in the Quantity box before you click the Transfer button. You will get multiple copies of the selected questions. The same note as above applies to questions that do not include variables; duplicate questions will appear on the test if multiple copies are requested.

Selecting Questions Randomly

To select questions randomly, you must view the testbank in Outline view.

Selecting from One Chapter or Section   Click on the title of the chapter, section, or problem type from which you want to randomly select questions. (Do *not* select an individual question reference.) Then enter the total number of questions you want in the Quantity box and click the Transfer button. The program will randomly select questions from those available under the heading you selected.

Selecting from Multiple Chapters or Sections   To randomly choose questions from more than one chapter or section, click on more than one chapter title or section by holding down the SHIFT key while you click. You can only select titles of the same type or level; for example, two chapter titles or two section titles. Then enter the total number of questions you want to select from *each* selected chapter or section in the Quantity box. When you click the Transfer button, the questions will be transferred to the test. This method can be used whether or not the testbank questions contain variable text or numbers.

Shuffling Multiple-Choice Answers

A setting in the TestWorks Preferences dialog box, accessed from the Setup menu, lets you decide whether or not to allow multiple-choice answers to automatically shuffle when multiple-choice questions are transferred from a testbank to a test. If Shuffle on Transfer is checked, the order of the answer choices in a test question will be different than they are in a testbank question. If it is not checked, the order of the answer choices in a test question will be the same as in the testbank question.

MODIFYING OR ADDING QUESTIONS

Modifying Questions

You can modify test questions in the same way that you modify testbank questions. Simply double-click on a question or select the question and click the Modify button to display the Question Editor. You can make changes in the question, answer, instruction, or descriptive information. Note that the changes you make in the test question will not affect the original version of the question in the testbank. The Question Editor is described in detail in the "Using the Question Editor" chapter of this Guide.

Adding Questions

You can add your own new questions to any test. In either Outline view or Question view, go to the part of the test where you want to add a question. Click once on a question to select it. Click the Add button and the Question Editor window will open. Choose a question type from the pull-down menu and then begin entering your question and answer.

If your questions are in User-Defined Order, your new question will be added after or before the selected question depending on the setting of the State button in the Main window.

If your questions are in a SmartSort Order, your new question will be added to the test in a location that follows the rules of the SmartSort.

REGENERATING AND LOCKING VARIABLE VALUES

Regenerating and locking values are two functions that apply only to test questions that include randomized variables for numbers or text, most common in tests for mathematics. You can tell whether or not a question includes variables by displaying the #Var descriptor; if it is larger than 1, then the question can be displayed in more than one variation.

Regenerating Values in Selected Questions

When you transfer questions from a testbank to a test, the test questions will contain the same variable values as in the testbank. You can regenerate these values by selecting one or more questions and clicking the Regenerate button or by choosing Regenerate on the Tools menu. The variable values will change to a different set of numbers or text strings. These values will be the numbers you see when the test is printed. If you print more than one form of a test, you have the option of either keeping these values or regenerating them from form to form.

Locking Values in Selected Questions

If there are certain questions on a test that contain variable numbers or text, and you plan to print multiple forms of a test, a global setting in the Test Print Settings dialog box, accessed while the Test window is active by choosing Print from the File menu, allows you to preserve these values on all forms. To lock values for a few individual questions, simply click on one or more questions in the Test window that you want to keep static and then click the Lock button. A small lock icon will appear next to the question(s) you selected. *(NOTE: The lock symbol will not print on the test.)* To unlock a question and make it dynamic again, select the question and click on the Lock button again.

SCRAMBLING TEST QUESTION ORDER

You may want to have TestWorks scramble the order of the questions on your test after you have chosen all the questions. If you click the Scramble button while a SmartSort is turned on, the questions on the test will be randomly mixed at the lowest level of sorting so that the SmartSort rules are still enforced.

For example, if the SmartSort is by Question Type, then questions of the same type will remain together on the test, but the order of questions within each question type will be scrambled.

Or, if the SmartSort is by Testbank Order, and the testbank has chapters, sections, and problem types, then the order of the questions within each problem type will be scrambled.

Or, if you are using a Custom SmartSort and sorting only by Difficulty Level, then the order of the questions within each difficulty level will be scrambled.

If you have your test questions in a User-Defined Order and click the Scramble button, the questions on the test will be scrambled at random to produce the new order. No grouping will occur. This may or may not produce desirable results, depending on the types of questions on the test.

MODIFYING THE TEST DISPLAY AND FORMAT

When you view a test in Question view, you are looking at the pages of the test as they will be printed. You can change the way the pages look and choose which information gets displayed by choosing Display or Format on the Setup menu.

Test Page Display Options

Click the Display button or choose Display on the Setup menu to view the Test Page Display Options dialog box. After making your selections, click OK to close the dialog and apply the changes to your test. Click Cancel to exit without changes.

```
┌─────────────────────────────────────────────────────────┐
│                  Test Page Display Options                │
├─────────────────────────────────────────────────────────┤
│  ┌─────────────────────────────────────────────────────┐ │
│  │ Descriptors:                                         │ │
│  │  ☐ Page Reference    ☐ Topic         ☐ User 1       │ │
│  │  ☐ Difficulty Level  ☐ Skill         ☐ User 2       │ │
│  │  ☐ Workspace Value   ☐ Objective     ☐ Correct Answer│ │
│  │  ☐ # Of Variations   ☐ Question Type ☒ Answer Blanks │ │
│  └─────────────────────────────────────────────────────┘ │
│  ┌─────────────────────────────────────────────────────┐ │
│  │  ☐ Print bimodal questions as short answer           │ │
│  └─────────────────────────────────────────────────────┘ │
│  ┌─────────────────────────────────────────────────────┐ │
│  │  Number for first question:   [ 1 ]                  │ │
│  │  Number for first page:       [ 1 ]                  │ │
│  └─────────────────────────────────────────────────────┘ │
│  ┌─────────────────────────────────────────────────────┐ │
│  │  Margins:    Left:  [0.5] in.   Top:    [0.5] in.    │ │
│  │              Right: [0.5] in.   Bottom: [0.5] in.    │ │
│  │  Workspace:        ● None            ○ Single        │ │
│  │                    ○ Double          ○ Triple        │ │
│  └─────────────────────────────────────────────────────┘ │
│                                    [ OK ]    [ Cancel ]   │
└─────────────────────────────────────────────────────────┘
```

Descriptors   In the Descriptors section, click in the check box to put an X next to each item you want to appear with each question on the test page.

Form of Bimodal Questions   Clicking the check box to place an X next to "Print bimodal questions as short answer" causes all bimodal questions to be printed in short-answer format rather than multiple-choice format on tests. This global setting can be overridden for individual questions by clicking the Form button after selecting bimodal questions on tests.

Starting Question and Page Number   Enter a number of the first question on your test and the first page number. Normally, these will both be 1, but there may be cases where you want to start with a different number.

Margins   Enter decimal numbers for the size of each margin—top, bottom, left, and right. (NOTE: The values you enter will also appear in the Page Setup dialog which is described in the "Choosing the Page Setup Options" section of this Guide.)

Workspace   Click one of the radio buttons to indicate a global setting for workspace. Double or triple will assign a multiple of that number of lines of workspace to each question. Workspace is described in more detail in the "Editing Descriptors" section of this Guide.

Test Format Options

Choose Format on the Setup menu to display the Test Setup dialog that lets you customize the style for some of the test components.

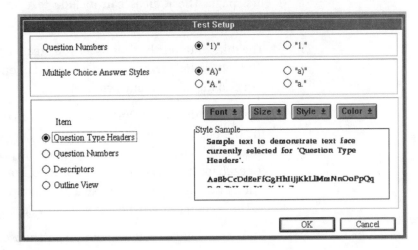

Styles for Question Numbers and Answer Choices   Click the radio button of your choice to indicate which style of question numbering you prefer for the test. Also click a radio button to select how you want multiple-choice answers to be labeled.

Font, Style, Size, and Color Choices   This dialog lets you define styles for question type headers, question numbers, descriptors, and Outline view on a test. First click the radio button next to the item you want to change. Then use the pull-down menus to choose a font, style, size, and color. You will see a sample in the style sample window. Repeat the style settings with other items as desired. Click OK to close the dialog and apply the changes to your test.

The Global Style Replacement option on the Format menu is used to change the font and type size of all the questions, answers, instructions, and various headers and footers on a test.

MODIFYING TEST HEADERS AND FOOTERS

You can customize both the test headers and footers and the question type headers that get printed on a test by choosing Page Headers or Question Type Headers on the Setup menu.

Page Headers and Footers   When you choose Page Headers on the Setup menu for a test, you will see the test Header and Footer Editor.

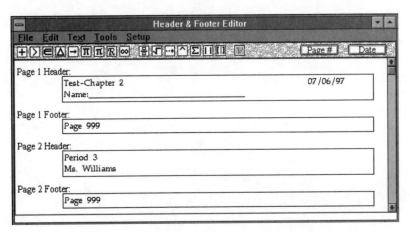

The first two sections let you create a title or header section for the top of the first page of your test and a page footer that gets printed at the bottom of the first page. These areas can include text and symbols and would usually include the test title, professor name, course number, date, page number, etc.

The third and fourth sections let you create a page header and a page footer that get printed on the second and subsequent pages of the test. These areas can also include text and symbols.

If you print different forms of a test, you can distinguish each form by inserting the page number in at least one of the areas in the Header and Footer Editor. A different letter of the alphabet will print as part of the page number for each form of the test that gets printed. For example, if you insert the page number in the Page 1 Footer area, the first form of the test will show Page A-1. The second form of the test will show Page B-1, etc.

Make the changes you want and then choose Close-Save Changes from the File menu.

Question Type Headers Question type headers are displayed and printed on tests whenever question type is one of the levels of sorting. For each type of question type, the program supplies a default instruction, but you can modify any of these headers as desired. When you choose Question Type Headers on the Setup menu for a test, you will see the Question Type Header dialog.

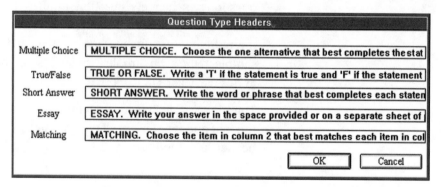

These fields can only include text. Make the changes you want and then click OK to apply the changes. Click Cancel to exit without changing.

SAVING A TEST

When you create a new test, you give it a name and the Test window appears, but there are no questions in the Test window. After you transfer questions to the test, you might want to save it for use at a later time. Tests are automatically saved when you close the Test window or when you exit the program.

If you make changes to a test and want to save it using a different name, choose the Save As command on the File menu. This will let you save a copy of the test using a name different from the original. The test will be saved with a **.TST** extension so you can find it easily when you open it at a later time. On Macintosh, you may opt to add the .TST extension, or not.

OPENING AN EXISTING TEST

To open a previously saved test, choose Open Test on the File menu. In the file dialog, locate the test you want to open, select, and click OK or Open. TestWorks tests on Windows are easy to locate because they are automatically given a .TST extension when named. It is advised to add the same extension on Macintosh test files to make them easy to recognize.

Using the Question Editor

You can modify any testbank or test question or add your own new test items by using the built-in Question Editor. The Question Editor lets you work with multiple-choice, true/false, short-answer, essay, matching, and bimodal types of questions.

MC   **multiple-choice**   standard question type with up to 5 answer choices, one or more correct answers

TF   **true/false**   standard true/false question type

SA   **short-answer**   standard question type used for fill-in or completion questions

ES   **essay**   standard question type used when sentences or paragraph answers are expected

MA   **matching**   questions are displayed in two columns with questions in Column 1 and answer choices in Column 2

BI   **bimodal**   questions are entered in multiple-choice format but can also be displayed in short-answer format

(NOTE: The prepackaged TestWorks testbank for any specific textbook will usually not include questions of all types, but all question types can be created by the user.)

With the Question Editor, you can insert math symbols, math expressions, mathematical graphs, and other graphic objects. You can even define variables within a question so that numbers and/or text can vary when you print multiple forms of a test.

OPENING THE QUESTION EDITOR

You can open the Question Editor window in any of the following ways.

1. Double-click on a question in a testbank or test that you want to edit. The question will be displayed in the Question Editor window.

2. Click once on a question then click the Modify button, or choose Modify from the Edit menu.

3. Click once on a question, then click the Add button on the Main window or choose Add After (or Add Before depending on the State button) on the Edit menu. The Question Editor window will be displayed as a blank form.

When adding new questions, you choose the type of question you want by selecting from the pull-down menu in the upper left corner of the Question Editor window. The question form you see in the Question Editor window varies with the question type you select. The forms, which are shown below, have some common elements, such as instructions, page references, difficulty level, workspace, and other descriptors, which are described in the "Editing Descriptors" section of this Guide.

MULTIPLE-CHOICE AND BIMODAL QUESTIONS

Multiple-choice (MC) questions and Bimodal (BI) questions use the same editing form which includes an optional Instruction field, a Question field, and five Answer choice fields.

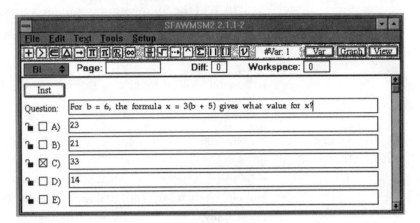

Type the stem of a multiple-choice question in the Question field and the answer choices in fields A, B, C, D, and E. Not all answer fields must be used, but start by entering choice A and do not leave any blank choices between other choices. After entering the answer choices, click the check box next to the correct answer. (More than one answer choice may be correct.)

Locking Answer Choices

The order of the answer choices can be shuffled when a test is printed. You may want some types of answer choices, such as "None of the above," not to be listed in a different order. Click on the lock to the left of any answer choice to prevent it from being moved. When the lock is closed, the answer choice is locked in place, while unlocked answer choices are shuffled.

When to Use Bimodal Questions

The Bimodal question type provides flexibility in your testbank and test questions because a question may be displayed in either multiple-choice or short-answer format on a test. Be sure BI is selected on the question type menu.

A good bimodal question is one that can be answered without seeing the multiple-choice answers. For example, the following question works well in short-answer format, so it would be a good bimodal question. It can be answered when the answer choices are not visible.

Multiple-Choice Format:

A(n) _____ triangle is one with exactly two congruent sides.
A) equilateral
B) isosceles
C) scalene
D) right

Short-Answer Format:

A(n) _____ triangle is one with exactly two congruent sides.

The following question stems work well in multiple-choice format, but usually *not* in short-answer format when the answer choices are removed, so they would not be suitable as bimodal question stems.

Which of the following statements is true?

All of the following statements are true, *except:*

Describe . . .

In general, do not make a question bimodal that would be "unfair" for the student to answer in its short-answer form.

Changing the Form of Bimodal Questions

All bimodal questions are entered and displayed as multiple-choice questions in the Question Editor. In testbanks and on tests, a nonprinting bullet symbol (•) indicates which test questions are bimodal questions. You can globally change how bimodal questions are displayed on tests by choosing the Display option from the Setup menu when the Test window is active, then clicking the check box next to "Print bimodal questions as short answer" on the Test Page Display Options dialog. In addition, you can override this global setting for individual questions by selecting them on the test and clicking the Form button. The bullet symbol becomes a tilde (~) to indicate that the form of the question has been changed from the global setting.

TRUE/FALSE QUESTIONS

True/false (TF) questions include an optional Instruction field, a Question field, and an answer.

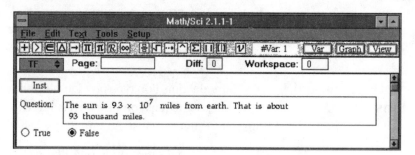

For true/false questions, enter the question statement in the Question field. Click the radio button next to True or False to indicate the correct answer.

SHORT-ANSWER AND ESSAY QUESTIONS

Short-answer (SA) and essay (ES) questions include an optional Instruction field, a Question field, and an Answer field. Both question types use the same form for entering questions.

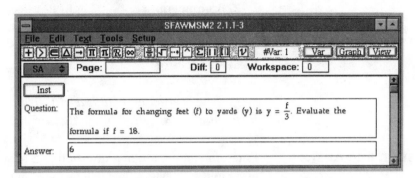

Use the short-answer question type for fill-in or completion statements, where the question can be answered with one or two words or a short phrase. Use the essay question type when longer sentences or paragraphs are expected as answers. Enter the question in the Question field and the correct answer in the Answer field.

MATCHING QUESTIONS

Matching (MA) questions include an Instructions field, a Question field, an Answer field, and an optional Foil field.

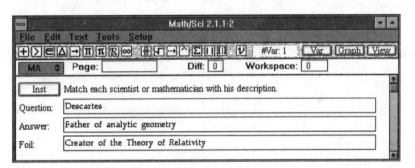

Using Instructions in Matching Questions

Matching questions *require* the use of a unique Instruction that will link related questions and ensure that they are grouped together when printed on a test. When you create a test, you will choose two or more matching questions for the test, and questions with the same Instruction will appear in the same set of matching questions. For Instructions, use a statement that is unique to the content of the questions. For example, let's say you enter five matching questions and they all share the same Instruction: "Match each scientist or mathematician with his description." The matching questions will be displayed on the test as shown below.

Match each scientist or mathematician with his description.

Column 1	Column 2
1) Newton	A) Constructed first satisfactory telescope
2) Brahmagupta	B) Physicist and an inventor of calculus
3) Galileo	C) Father of analytic geometry
4) Descartes	D) Inventor of fractals
5) Mandelbrot	E) 7th century algebraist and astronomer

(NOTE: The Instruction field is a "list" field, and details for working with the Instruction list are given in the "Editing Instructions" section of this Guide.)

Question and Answer

Enter only one matching question and answer on the form. Whatever you enter in the Question field will be listed in Column 1, the left column, when the matching questions are displayed on a test. Whatever you enter in the Answer field will be displayed in Column 2, the right column, as a possible answer choice for all the questions in the group of matching questions that have been selected for a test.

If two matching questions selected for a test have the same correct answer, the answer choice will only appear once in the Column 2 list of answer choices. So, it may be possible to have, for example, ten items in Column 1 and only two choices in Column 2 if the correct answers for the ten items are either, for example, "best represented by line graph" or "best represented by circle graph."

Using Answer Foils

The Foil field may be used to add additional, but wrong, choices to Column 2 of any matching exercise if that question is selected for a test. When foils are used, it is possible for Column 2 to have more items than Column 1, since Column 2 will include some choices that do not match with any item in Column 1.

Using the given example, if two of the questions included foils of "Greatest mathematician of ancient Greece" and "Creator of the Theory of Relativity," the matching questions will be displayed on the test as shown below.

Match each scientist or mathematician with his description.

Column 1	Column 2
1) Newton	A) Constructed first satisfactory telescope
2) Brahmagupta	B) Physicist and an inventor of calculus
3) Galileo	C) Greatest mathematician of ancient Greece
4) Descartes	D) Inventor of fractals
5) Mandelbrot	E) Creator of the Theory of Relativity
	F) Father of analytic geometry
	G) 7th century algebraist and astronomer

Answer choices in Column 2 are randomly ordered so that the correct answer is usually not directly across from the question that matches it. Due to randomness, however, it might be possible for a choice to be directly across from its match, but having one or more occurrences of this is highly unlikely, especially in longer sets of questions.

TYPING AND ALIGNING TEXT

Typing Text

In the Question Editor, to begin typing in a question, answer, or answer choice field, move the mouse pointer over the field where you want to enter text and click the mouse to position the cursor and begin typing, just as you would with any word processor. Do not press ENTER or RETURN at the end of any line unless you want to force a carriage return. Long sentences and paragraphs will be reformatted to fit the width of the question space when the question is displayed or printed on a test or in a testbank.

To edit text, first select the text you want to edit by holding down the mouse button and dragging the cursor across the text to highlight it. Then you can choose Copy or Cut from the Edit menu or assign a Font, Size, Style, or Color from the Text menu. If text has been copied or cut, it can be pasted at the current location of the cursor by choosing Paste from the Edit menu.

For information on keyboard shortcuts that can be used while editing, see the "Keyboard Shortcuts" section of this Guide.

Using the Ruler

While entering a question, you may need to adjust the margins, tabs, or text justification within a field to set up special spacing or alignment, for a table, for example. Choose Show Ruler on the Edit menu to display the ruler if it is not visible at the top of the Question Editor window.

Using Tabs The ruler displays the full width of the area that is allowed for the question. The four triangles at the left side of the ruler can be dragged onto the ruler to set tabs at any location. Each triangle symbol represents a different kind of tab: left-justified, center-justified, right-justified, and a special tab to align equal signs or decimal points.

(NOTE: The tabs do not affect the margins set for a page. If page margins are set too wide, this may cause some lines of tables and tabbed material to wrap to the next line. Be sure to set page margins small when questions contain large tables or tabbed columns. When you create questions, avoid making table material wider than the normal page width.)

Using Text Justification Buttons Underneath the four triangle tabs are the four text justification buttons to produce left-justified text, center-justified text, right-justified text, or even-justified text, respectively.

When you want to set the justification for a paragraph of text you are going to type, place your cursor in a field and then click one of the buttons to set the justification.

USING SPECIAL SYMBOLS AND TEMPLATES

While you are entering a question, if you need to insert a symbol that is not available on the keyboard, you might be able to find the symbol on one of the symbol palettes that are located across the top of the Question Editor window. If the symbol palettes are not visible, choose Show Symbols from the Tools menu in the Question Editor.

Symbol Palettes

The nine symbol palettes are drop down menus that contain related symbols that you can click to insert at the cursor location.

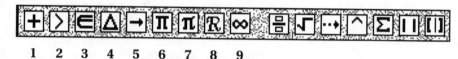

1 mathematical operations, composition, abstract algebra
2 equality, approximate equality, inequalities
3 sets, proofs, logic
4 geometric figures and symbols
5 arrows, segments
6 capital Greek alphabet
7 lowercase Greek alphabet
8 number sets
9 infinity symbol, degree symbol, script "l," and others

Math Templates

For subjects such as mathematics, statistics, chemistry, and economics, you may need to insert a mathematical expression into a question or answer. Use the math templates located at the top of the Question Editor window. If the symbols and template buttons are not showing, choose Show Symbols on the Tools menu.

The seven template buttons each display a palette of mathematical or scientific expressions that contain slots, or fields, for you to enter numbers or text. The expressions grow or change size dynamically as you enter numbers or text in any of the fields.

1 fractions, mixed numbers, superscripts, subscripts, grouping box
2 radicals, long division, synthetic division, sinking funds, annuities
3 over and under bars, braces, rays, lines, arcs
4 hat, tilde, cross-out, primes
5 integrals, summation, coproduct
6 parentheses, vertical bars, double bars, braces, brackets
7 determinants, matrices, charts, tables

When you want to insert a template at the location of the cursor, click on the appropriate button to display the palette. Then click a template to insert it into the question. Boxes outline the fields where you can enter numbers, text, or other templates into the template. To move from field to field within a template, press the right arrow key or click in any field with the mouse. When you have filled all the fields, press the right arrow key again to move out of the template and continue typing.

Nested Templates   You may put one template inside of another template when necessary.

Example: $\dfrac{\sqrt{2}}{3}$

Create this expression by first choosing the fraction template. Place the cursor in the numerator of the fraction and then choose the square root template. Enter a number in the radical then press the right arrow to exit the square root template. Press the right arrow key again to exit the numerator or click in the denominator. Now type a number in the denominator. Press the right arrow to exit the fraction template.

DEFINING, INSERTING, AND VIEWING VARIABLES

To add more variability to your questions and to the testbank, you may want to create some questions that use variable text or numbers. You can generate different versions of these questions when you use the Regenerate button or when you print multiple forms of a test. Using a simple example, the question,

"Find the sum of 6 and 9."

is a static question that is always the same and always has the answer 15. But if 6 and 9 are replaced by variables, the question,

"Find the sum of **V1** and **V2**."

represents five different problems when V1, V2, and V3 (the answer) are defined as this set of linked variables:

V1 = 5,6,7,8,9
V2 = 7,5,8,6,9
V3 = 12,11,15,14,18

Each time the problem is printed, V1, V2, and V3 can have a different set of values depending on which value is randomly selected for V1.

Randomized Variable Feature Components

In the Question Editor, the *v* button, #Var, and Var button all are related to the randomized variable feature.

Number of Variations   The #Var information at the top of the Question Editor window tells how many variations are available for the current question. If the question does not include any variables, then the #Var will equal 1. When variables are included in the question, then the number of variations can range anywhere from 1 to 50+ (more than 50), depending on the number of variables and the range for each variable.

Inserting Variables In the Question Editor, to insert a variable into a question at the cursor location, click the *v* button and choose a variable from V1 to V20. Type the rest of the question, inserting additional variables as needed to indicated which words or numbers will be randomly selected from the values you define.

Defining and Linking Variables Each variable you insert into a question needs to be defined in terms of the values, either text or numbers, it can represent. To define variable values, click the Var button to display the Variable Definitions worksheet.

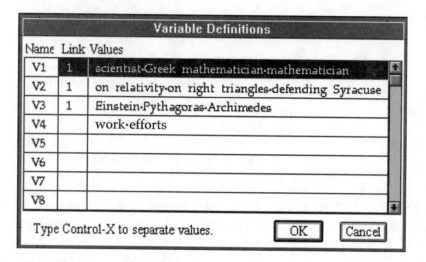

Click once to insert your cursor into a field and enter the values for the variable. Values can be numbers or text. Separate values by typing CTRL-X. A bullet symbol will appear.

The value for each variable will be randomly chosen from the set of values you enter on the worksheet, unless the variable is linked to another variable.

To link values, so that if a certain value is chosen for one variable then a related value is chosen for another variable, use the Link column. Enter the same value in the Link column for all the variables that are dependent on each other.

The example above shows that variables 1, 2, and 3 are linked, so that if "scientist" is selected for variable 1, then "on relativity" and "Einstein" will be used for variables 2 and 3 when they appear in the question. If the variables are not linked, then the word "scientist" or "Greek mathematician" or "mathematician" would be combined randomly with "on relativity," "on right triangles," or "defending Syracuse," and with a name, instead of linking the names with their occupations and accomplishments. The values for V4 are not linked to the other variables, so "work" or "efforts" will be chosen randomly from the set when V4 is used in the question.

Removing all the values for a variable on the worksheet will not remove the variable symbol from the question. When you return to the Question Editor, the variable will be displayed as "undefined."

Viewing Variables   When you define values for the variables in a problem, the Question Editor screen will replace the variable with one of the defined values. You can switch between two views of the question by clicking the View button. One mode will show the variable names, and the other will show the variable values. Using the variables defined above, the two modes would look like this in a question:

> **What V1 is well known for his V4 V2?**
> **Answer: V3**

> **What mathematician is well known for his efforts defending Syracuse?**
> **Answer: Archimedes**

Deleting Variables   To delete a variable you have inserted, simply move the cursor to the right of the variable and press the BACKSPACE or DELETE key. You may also select the variable and then choose Cut from the Edit menu. Deleting or cutting a variable from a question will not remove its definition on the Variable Definitions worksheet.

Uneditable Variables   In testbanks prepared by the Publisher, some questions may display variables that are uneditable. These variables are usually associated with complicated mathematical calculations that use features beyond the scope of the TestWorks program. The Publisher-defined variables will be displayed on the screen as Vs without reference numbers. *(CAUTION: Altering or deleting these variables may corrupt the mathematical calculations in the question or answer so that the question becomes incorrect and unusable.)*

INSERTING GRAPHICS

When you want to insert a graphic into a question, place the cursor where you want to insert the graphic, then choose Import Graphic from the Tools menu in the Question Editor. TestWorks can import graphics in the following formats: BMP, GIF, TIFF, PCX (Windows), PICT (Macintosh). Only graphics imported in PCX format will print at higher resolutions. For best performance, restrict your PCX graphics to 200 dpi or less.

Using the file dialog box, choose the graphic file you want to import and click OK. Next, you will see the Import Graphics dialog.

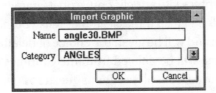

Store the graphic in a specific category of the Graphics Library. Use one of the existing category names in the pull-down menu or type a new category name in the space provided. You may change the name of the graphic file at this point. Click OK to display the graphic in your question. Graphics can be cut, copied, and pasted, or moved in the same way as other text or objects in the field.

Using the Graphics Library

Graphics you insert into a question are automatically saved in the testbank's or test's Graphics Library so that they can be reused in other questions. The advantage is that a graphic stored in the Graphics Library is stored only once instead of being saved with every question that uses it. This saves space on disk and in memory, and will make it easier to maintain the graphic files if changes are necessary. You will need to replace the graphic in only one place and it will be updated in all the questions that use the graphic.

In the Graphics Library dialog, you will see the filename of the graphic file in the category you chose to store it. There may also be other category names in which other graphics are stored.

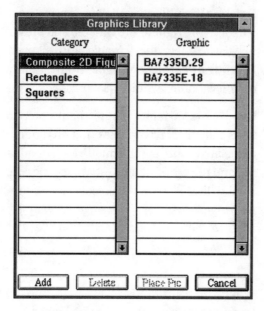

Selecting an Object from the Graphics Library To select a graphic from the Graphics Library, place the cursor where you want to insert the graphic and choose Graphics Library from the Tools menu in the Question Editor. Find the graphic file you would like and click the Place Pic button to place the graphic in the question.

Removing an Object from the Graphics Library To remove an object from the Graphics Library, click once on its name and then click the Delete button. You will be given a message that tells you how many questions contain the graphic and will be given the choice of deleting it from all. If you click OK, the file name will be deleted from the Graphics Library list and the graphic will be removed from all pertinent questions.

Setting Attributes for Graphics

In TestWorks, each graphic you insert is inserted as a text character or as a transparent object. You can select one of these as a global attribute for graphics by choosing Preferences on the Setup menu. In future versions of the program, you will also be able to insert a graphic as an excluded object, currently disabled in the Preferences dialog box.

As text characters, graphics become part of the paragraph of text and can be positioned in the same way as other text in the question. They will move if spaces, tabs, or carriage returns preceding them are inserted or deleted. No text will print in the same space as the graphic.

As a transparent object, text entered will be superimposed on the graphic.

USING THE GRAPHING TOOL

You can create graphs of functions and relations on Cartesian or polar axes, or create number line graphs by using TestWorks' built-in Graphing Tool. Open the Question Editor for the question you want to create or edit and put the cursor in one of the fields for the question. Then click the Graph button or choose Create Graph on the Tools menu. To edit an existing graph, double-click on it to open the Graph window.

The Graph Window

The Graph window contains the graph or graphs that will be inserted into the question. Menu options and buttons at the top of the screen allow you to modify the graph, print the graph, place the graph in a problem, or exit the graphing tool.

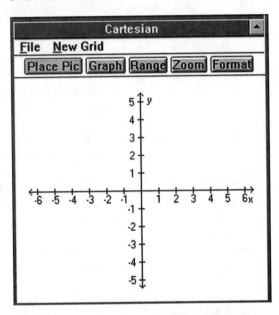

File Menu   Choose Print on the File menu to print the contents of the Graph window. Choose Quit on the File menu to close the Graphing Tool without placing the graphic in the question.

New Grid Type   The New Grid menu lets you choose one of three different axes for the graph: Cartesian, Polar, or Number Line. The appropriate set of axes will appear when you make your selection. The types of functions and relations you can define and graph are based on the grid type you select. (*NOTE: If you choose one grid type and plot a graph, then change to another grid type, the graphs on the first grid will be erased.*)

Graph Button   Click the Graph button to display the Set Up Graphs window (see next section). You define or edit functions or other items for the list by choosing an equation type on the Add menu. You display the defined graphs by clicking the Plot box and then the Apply button.

Range Button   The Range button lets you adjust the viewing area for the Graph window by choosing either the center point value or the bottom or left point value.

Click one of the radio buttons and fill in positive or negative coordinates for the point you want to position. Click Apply to see the results without closing the Range dialog. Click OK to apply the results and close the Range dialog. Click Cancel to close the Range dialog without making a change.

Zoom Button   The Zoom button lets you zoom in or out to show more or less detail in the graph that shows in the Graph window.

Enter a zoom factor from 2 to 99 then click either the Zoom In or Zoom Out button as many times as you wish without closing the Zoom dialog. Click OK to apply the results and close the Zoom dialog. Click Cancel to close the Zoom dialog without making a change.

Format Button   The Format button lets you adjust the spacing of the tick marks, the scale, the labeling, the width of the axes, and the background pattern for a graph. The Format dialog varies slightly depending on whether you have chosen a Cartesian, polar, or number line type of grid.

Pixels per Tick	This number determines how far apart the tick marks are on each axis. The default value is 20. To move tick marks closer together, choose a number smaller than 20. To move tick marks farther apart, choose a number larger than 20.
Scale (units per tick)	This number determines how many units are represented by each tick mark. The default value is 1.
Ticks per label	This number determines which tick marks are labeled with a number value. To label every tick mark, enter 1.
Label	Enter the letters you want to use to label each axis. The default for Cartesian is x and y. The default for polar is r.
Show tick marks	Click in the check box to remove the X if you do not want tick marks to show.
Label tick mark	Click in the check box to remove the X if you do not want tick marks to be labeled.
Label size	Enter the point size you want for the labels. The allowable range is from 10 to 24 point.
Axis width	Choose a thin or thick line for the axis or axes in the graph.
Background	Choose dotted, lined, or blank for the background of the Cartesian graph.

Place Pic Button When the Graph window shows the picture of the graph you want to use, click the Place Pic button to insert the contents of the Graph window into your question. The Graphing Tool will close automatically.

Changing the Size of the Graph Window You can adjust the size of the Graph window to show more or less of each axis used in the graph. In the Windows version, one way to change the size is to grab the lower right corner of the Graph window with the double arrow mouse pointer and drag it to the desired location. In both Windows and Macintosh versions, you can double-click on the Graph window to open the Resize dialog where you can specify the width and height of the window. Try to make the graphic only as large as necessary in order to save disk space and printing time. For consistency, use the standard default size of the Graph window.

The Set Up Graphs Window

The Set Up Graphs window is used to define and display the functions or other items that can appear in the Graph window. When you choose a graph type from the Add menu, you will see a dialog where you can define the graph. The Add menu varies, depending on which grid type you have chosen. The number of elements (function graphs, points, lines, segments, etc.) is limited to 10.

Add Menu (Cartesian)

y = Enter an equation in terms of x.

x = Enter an equation in terms of y.

Parabola	Choose one of the four forms of the equation. Equations that include a, but not h and k, have vertex at (0,0). Equations that include h and k have vertex at (h,k). Enter values for a or a, h, and k.
Circle	Choose one of the two forms of the equation. Equations that include r, but not h and k, have center at (0,0). Equations that include h and k have center at (h,k). Enter values for r or r, h, and k.
Ellipse	Choose one of the two forms of the equation. Equations that include a and b, but not h and k, have center at (0,0). Equations that include h and k have center at (h,k). Enter values for a and b, or a, b, h, and k.
Hyperbola	Choose one of the four forms of the equation. Equations that include a and b, but not h and k, have center at (0,0). Equations that include h and k have center at (h,k). Enter values for a and b, or a, b, h, and k.
Point (x,y)	Enter coordinates for x and y. Choose style and labeling preferences.
Segment	Enter the coordinates for the two endpoints. Choose style and labeling preferences.
Parametric	Enter two equations in terms of t. Enter minimum and maximum for values of t.

Add Menu (Polar)

r =   Enter a function using "theta" as the variable. To type a theta symbol, press ALT-O (the letter "o") in Windows or OPTION-O on Macintosh.

Point (x,y)   Enter the coordinates of the point (x,y). Choose style and labeling preferences.

Add Menu (Number Line)

Point   Enter the coordinate of the point on the number line. Choose style and labeling preferences.

Segment   Enter the coordinates of two points on the number line. Choose style and labeling preferences.

Ray   Enter the coordinates of the endpoint. Also choose whether you want the ray to point left or right. Choose style and labeling preferences.

Line   Pick a pattern and color for the line.

Delete Button   To remove an item from the Set Up Graphs window, click once on the item's description to select it, then click the Delete button.

Trace Button   To see the coordinates for a point on any of the functions displayed in the Cartesian or Polar Graph window, click the Trace button so that it says Trace On. The words "Trace coordinates" will appear at the top of the Graph window.

Click on the description of the function you want to trace. Then use the left and right arrow keys to move the crosshairs along the graph and view the coordinates of the point. To make the crosshairs move a bigger step, hold down the SHIFT key when you press the right or left arrow key.

If a graph has two branches, such as in a hyperbola, press the TAB key to move the crosshairs from one branch of the graph to the other. This will also work for circles and ellipses.

To move the crosshairs to a different graph, click on its description in the Set Up Graphs window. You may need to press the right or left arrow key several times to make the crosshairs appear for any given graph.

Compound Button   When you graph two or more inequalities, you can shade the intersection of the graphs by using the Compound button. First define the inequalities, but do not graph them. Then click the Compound button and choose which inequalities you want to compound. When you click OK, the compounded statement will appear in the Set Up Graphs window. Click the check box and then Apply to see the intersection of the two graphs.

Defining Functions

On many of the function definition screens, there are pull-down menus that let you change the look of the graph.

Relation Menu Many equations can be defined as either equalities or inequalities. To choose the relation you want to graph, choose a symbol on the Relation menu.

Pattern Menu Lines and curves can be graphed as solid lines or some type of dashed pattern. Make your choice from the Pattern menu.

Color Menu Points, lines, and curves can be graphed in black or a choice of colors. Make your selection from the Color menu. *(NOTE: Colored items on tests will print as shades of gray if you do not use a color printer for your test.)*

Shade Menu When graphing an inequality, you can choose a pattern for the shading that shows which side of the curve or line is included in the graph. Make your selection from the Shade menu.

Entering a Function To type a function or relation, type the numbers and letters from the keyboard. Some symbols can be typed with a combination of keys from the keyboard:

infinity   Type ALT-I (Windows) or OPTION-I (Macintosh)

theta   Type ALT-O (Windows) or OPTION-O (Macintosh)

pi   Type ALT-P (Windows) or OPTION-P (Macintosh)

fraction   Type a slash (/) for the fraction bar. Use parentheses where needed to group symbols.

exponent   Type the caret symbol (^) to indicate exponentiation.

Using Built-In Functions Some symbols are already defined in the list on the right side of each function definition window. You can just scroll to the symbol you want and click on it to make it part of your equation.

Continuity You can decrease the time it takes to graph a function by selecting the appropriate description of its continuity. If you do not know if a function is continuous, and click the Might Be Continuous button.

Domain You can specify the domain you want to use for any graph by entering a Minimum and Maximum value for the x variable. In most cases, you will want the domain of the function or relation to stretch from -inf to +inf, which are the defaults for the Minimum and Maximum values.

Speed vs. Accuracy The sliding accuracy scale on some dialogs lets you choose to display a graph faster or with more accuracy. If you choose Faster, the program will plot fewer points to display the graph. If you choose More Accurate, the program will plot more points to display the graph. In some cases, it will take slightly more time to plot a graph more accurately. In many cases, you will not notice a distinct time difference between the settings.

EDITING INSTRUCTIONS

The Instruction field in each question type is an optional field that can contain text, expressions, and graphics that apply to a single question or a set of questions in a testbank. Each instruction that you enter becomes part of an instruction list so that the same instruction can be assigned to more than one question and those questions can be grouped together on a test. Instructions should always be used, for example, for sets of matching questions and for questions. *(NOTE: Instruction lines may or may not be preassigned to questions in the testbank for your textbook.)*

Modifying List Items

If an instruction already appears in the Editor window for a question, you can click the Inst button to display the Instruction List where the current instruction will be highlighted in the list. Click the Edit button to display the Instruction Editor.

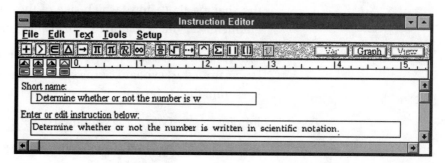

The full text of the instruction is displayed in the lower edit box and you can change it in any way you want. You can insert symbols, graphics, templates, graphs, and text in the instruction, just as in the question itself. The box will grow and shrink to fit the instruction.

By default, the Short Name for the instruction is the same as the first 60 characters of the instruction. This is what will appear in the Instruction list and in most cases, will be descriptive enough to let you identify the instruction. You may change the short name for the instruction so that what shows up in the Instruction list will be more descriptive. For example, if the Instruction contains only a figure or a table, you might want to assign a short name of "Figure 3-01" or "Table 3.2," which identifies the chapter number, section, or figure number.

(NOTE: When you change an instruction, the change will take place for all the questions that are currently assigned to that instruction. You do not need to edit the instruction in more than one place.)

Choosing an Item from the List

If no instruction appears in the Instruction field for a question, you can assign an instruction by clicking the Inst button. When the Instruction list appears, scroll through the list and select the instruction you want. Then click the Choose button to close the Instruction list and insert the instruction into the current question.

Adding Items to the List   If no instruction appears in the Instruction field for a question, and you do not see the instruction you want in the Instruction list, click the Add button. This will open a blank Instruction Editor for you to enter a new instruction. Enter the instruction and a short name, if desired. On the File menu, choose Close–Save Changes to save the new instruction in the Instruction list. Choose the new instruction from the list to place it in the current question.

Deleting Items from the List   To delete items from the Instruction list, select the item and then click the Delete button. You will be given a message that states how many questions contain this instruction and asks if you want to delete the instruction from all. If you click OK, the instruction will be deleted from the list and from all the testbank questions to which the instruction is currently assigned.

Clearing   To remove an instruction from the Instruction field of a question, but not remove the instruction from the Instruction list, click the Inst button to display the Instruction list. The current instruction will be highlighted. Click the Clear button to remove the instruction from the current question. The instruction will remain in the Instruction list and remain attached to other assigned questions.

EDITING DESCRIPTORS   Each question in a testbank can have descriptive information assigned to it to aid in identifying the question's purpose or location. This information includes a page reference, difficulty level, amount of workspace, topic, skill, objective, and two additional user-defined categories. Usually some, but not all, descriptive information is provided in the program for any specific textbook. Other descriptive information may be entered by the user.

Page Reference   This text field contains the page numbers of the textbook where the answer to the question is found or explained. It can be a single number or a range of numbers.

Difficulty Level   This text field contains a number that describes the difficulty level of the question from 0 to 9. A "0" means that no difficulty level has been assigned. The relative value of the numbers assigned can vary from testbank to testbank. Some may use a rating scale of 1-easy, 2-average, 3-hard, while others may use 1, 2, 3, 4, 5, or other combination of numbers.

Workspace   This text field contains a number that determines the number of blank lines that should be printed following the question on a test if the workspace option is requested. The actual measured space will vary with the font and type size that is used for the question, but in general, for a 10-point type, 6 lines equals 1 inch of space.

Topic, Skill, Objective   These three fields are list fields that assign a topic, skill, or objective to a question. List items can be entered and then assigned to one or more questions. You can add, edit, delete, or clear items in these lists in the same way as the Instruction field, except that these fields can contain only text.

User 1, User 2

These two fields are user-defined list fields that assign additional descriptive information to a question; this will vary from testbank to testbank. List items can be entered and then assigned to one or more questions. You can add, edit, delete, or clear items in these lists in the same way as the Instruction field, except that these fields can contain only text.

SAVING QUESTIONS AND CLOSING THE EDITOR

Once you have created a new question or have modified an existing question and you wish to close the Question Editor and return to the Book window, you can either save or cancel what you have done. If you double-click (single-click on Macintosh) on the close box in the upper left corner of the window or choose Close–Save Changes from the File menu, you will get feedback that your new question or edits are being saved. If you choose Close–Cancel Changes, everything you did while in the Question Editor will be disregarded.

Printing Tests and Testbanks

This section discusses how to print testbanks, tests, and answer keys. *(NOTE: Graphics-heavy tests, common for some subject matters, will print more slowly than tests with fewer graphics.)*

CHOOSING THE PAGE SETUP OPTIONS

To set the paper size, margins, orientation, or scaling that will be used when you print a testbank or test, choose Page Setup under the File menu.

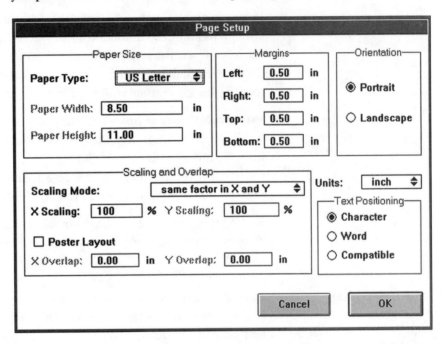

(NOTE: This dialog will vary depending on your computer and operating system.)

SETTING THE TEST PRINT OPTIONS

When you are ready to print a test, first be sure the Test window is active by clicking on it. Its title bar should be dark in Windows or gray on Macintosh. Then choose Print on the File menu.

Forms of a Test and Answer Key

You can print up to 25 different forms, or versions, of a test to distribute to different students or different classes. The forms can vary in different ways depending on the question types you selected, the variability of each question, and the settings for the following three options:

Preserve question order   If this check box has an X in it, the questions on each form of the test will be in the same order as on the first form of the test. If there is no X in the box, the questions will be randomly scrambled at the lowest level of organizational sorting.

Preserve number values   If this check box has an X in it, the questions that contain randomized numbers or text will *not* be regenerated. All the forms of the test will use the same values as the first form of the test. If there is no X in the check box, the variables in each question will be regenerated so that each form of the text contains different number or text values.

Preserve MC answer order   If your test contains multiple-choice questions or bimodal questions in multiple-choice format, and the check box has an X in it, the order of the answer choices on all the forms will be the same as on the first form of the test. If there is no X in the check box, the multiple-choice answers will be randomly reordered on each form of the test.

Printed forms of a test can be distinguished by an identifying letter that gets printed as part of the page number. For more information, refer to the "Modifying Test Headers and Footers" section of this Guide.

Print Answer Key

Place an X in the check box to print an answer key for each form. Check other boxes as desired to determine which information, in addition to the answers, gets printed for each question.

Printing the Test

Click OK in the Testbank Print Settings dialog to accept the print settings you want. You will then see the standard print dialog for your system where you can set other print options such as the range of pages to print.

SETTING THE TESTBANK PRINT OPTIONS

When you want to print a testbank, be sure the Book window is active, then choose Print on the File menu. Click OK when all the settings are correct.

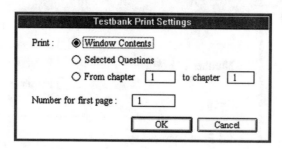

Print Window Contents   If you are in Question view, the program will print all the questions in the section that is currently shown in the Book window. If you are in Outline view, the program prints the outline for the book as it is shown on the screen, whether expanded or collapsed.

Print Selected Questions   This option prints only those items that are selected in the current window. (Hold down the SHIFT key and click on one or more questions to select them.)

Print a Range of Chapters   This option lets you print the questions from any or all of the chapters in a book. Click next to one of the radio buttons to print all chapters or a range of chapters. Be sure to enter the chapter numbers if you select to print a range.

Number for First Page   Enter a starting number for the page numbers that will print at the bottom of every page. Then click OK. Each chapter will begin printing on a new page.

Customizing TestWorks

TestWorks gives you the freedom to customize the way text and graphics are displayed and printed in a testbank or test. It also allows you to regenerate question values, sort testbank questions in a custom order, and reset values you specify.

DEFAULT STYLES FOR QUESTION EDITOR

Choose Editor Default Styles on the Setup menu to change the base font, type size, style, and color for new questions that are added to a testbank or test.

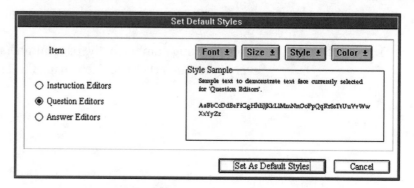

To set the default styles for the Instruction, Question, or Answer fields in the question editors, click one of the radio buttons and select a Font, Size, Style, and/or Color from the pull-down menus. You can see the effect of your choices in the Style Sample window.

(NOTE: The settings will be in effect for all new questions you add, but will not affect questions that are already part of the testbank or test.)

(CAUTION: Using this feature will permanently change the testbank and, in some cases, may take a while to complete. Make a backup of your testbank (the .BOK file) before attempting this procedure.)

Choose Global Style Replacement from the Setup menu to change the font and type size of all the questions, answers, instructions lines, headers and footers on a test.

FONTS AND STYLES FOR TESTBANK HEADINGS

Choose Page Headers on the Setup menu to choose a default font and style for page headers and footers that appear on Testbank pages. The Header and Footer Editor allows you to type text, choose symbols or math templates, and insert graphs into the areas for header and footer information. Odd headers and footers will be printed on each odd-numbered page, while even headers and footers will be printed on each even-numbered page when you print the testbank.

REGENERATING VARIABLES IN A TESTBANK

In testbanks that contain questions that include variable text or numbers, the numbers displayed in the testbank are saved with the testbank. Variable values can be regenerated when the questions are transferred to a test. They can also be regenerated in the testbank to display different text or numbers. To regenerate the values, select the chapter, section, or question you want to regenerate and click the Regenerate button. You can also choose Regenerate on the Tools menu.

(CAUTION: Using this feature will permanently change the testbank and, in some cases, may take a while to complete. Make a backup of your testbank (the .BOK file) before attempting this procedure. It is much easier and faster to regenerate variables of questions after they have been transferred to a test.)

RESETTING VALUES IN A TESTBANK

Choose Global Field Reset on the Setup menu or click the Reset button if you want to reset all the entries for the Difficulty Level, Page Reference, or Workspace to a specific value.

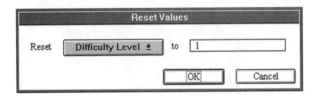

This feature is useful if you are creating a new testbank based on an existing testbank and want to clear out all the old values.

SORTING A TESTBANK

In some cases, especially after adding new questions, entering page references, or merging questions from two books, you may want to sort the questions in a testbank. Select the Book window, and switch to Outline view. Select one or more sections of the testbank, then choose Sort on the Tools menu.

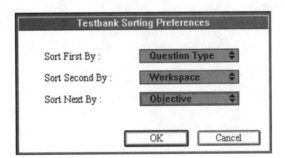

Select a sort order by choosing from the menus for first sort, second sort, and third sort. For example, in a testbank that is organized by chapter and question type, if you want to put the questions within each question type in order by page reference, select all the chapters, then choose:

Sort First By:	**Question Type**
Sort Second By:	**Page reference**
Sort Next By:	**None**

In another testbank that is organized by chapter, section, and problem type, if you want to put questions within each problem type in order by difficulty level, select one or more problem types, then choose:

Sort First By: **Difficulty Level**
Sort Second By: None
Sort Next By: None

(CAUTION: Using this feature will permanently change the testbank and, in some cases, may take a while to complete. Make a backup of your testbank (the .BOK file) before attempting this procedure.)

Creating a New Testbank

If you are a testbank author or if you want to create a new testbank that contains your own questions, you will need to create a New Book. This section discusses how to set up a new testbank structure, how to type header titles, add questions, and use the convenient spell checker.

See the "General Description of TestWorks" section of this Guide for more details on the buttons and menu choices that follow.

TESTBANK SETUP

In order to create a new testbank, you must first decide how the testbank will be organized, assign the testbank a name, name and describe each organizational level, and assign default styles for various parts of the testbank. Except for the number of levels, the names, descriptions, and styles can be changed at any time.

Number of Levels

When you choose New Book on the File menu, the first dialog you see asks for the number of levels.

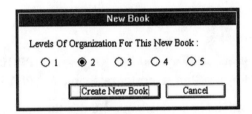

To determine the number of levels in the testbank, decide how the questions will be organized. Each level of organization will be assigned a name and have a specific type of heading when the testbank is viewed. The questions would be grouped under the lowest level of headings. Although you can use up to 5 levels, the two most common organizational schemes are:

Headings	Number of levels
Chapter, Question Type	2
Chapter, Section, Question Type	3

Click OK to confirm the number of levels and move to the book setup dialog.

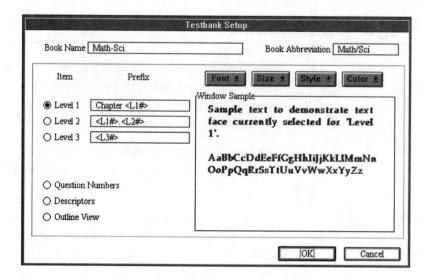

Testbank Name and Abbreviation

In the Book Name field, enter the book title on which the testbank questions are based. Include the book title, edition, and author. You are able to type up to 60 characters. In the Book Abbreviation field, enter a six-character or less abbreviation for the book title which will be used as part of the unique ID assigned to each question in the testbank.

Examples:

Probability testbank	**PROB**
Physics, 2nd semester testbank	**PHYS2**

Questions in the testbank will use the book abbreviation and the number of levels to create the unique ID for each question. The question ID "PROB 1.1-5" refers to the fifth question in chapter 1, section 1 of the Probability testbank.

Styles for Levels of Organization

Titles for the organizational levels of the testbank will be shown when the testbank is displayed in either Outline view or Question view. How the titles are formatted depends on how they are set up in the book setup dialog. Each level of organization can have a different font, type size, style, and color.

To define the style for each level, first click the radio button next to the item. In the Prefix box, type any text you want to precede each title when it is shown on the screen. If you want to include the number of the item, type <L1#>, using the appropriate number for the level number you want. You will see the effects of your entries in the Style Sample window.

Do not enter the titles for chapters, sections, and so on, here because you will enter them when you enter the questions associated with them.

Styles for Headers, Descriptors, and Outline View

Click the radio button next to each of the items and choose a font, size, style, and color default for each one. This will set the defaults for the headers, descriptors, and Outline view of the testbank.

ADDING TITLES AND QUESTIONS

When you click OK on the Setup dialog, your new testbank will appear as a Book window in Outline view. The Book window will contain a heading for each level you defined in the Setup dialog, including prefixes and numbers.

Editing Titles

To edit the title for any of the levels, double-click on the heading or click once to select the heading then click on the Modify button in the Main window. Either action will open the Header Editor window. Enter the chapter or section title and click OK. In the Book window, you should see the title along with the prefix that you specified in the Book Setup dialog. Enter and edit other titles in the same way.

Adding Additional Titles

To add additional chapter, section, or subsection titles, click on the type of title you want to add, then click on the Add button in the Main window or choose Add After (or Add Before) from the Edit menu. A Header Editor window will open and you can type the title. For example to add a title for chapter 2, select Chapter 1 and choose Add After; to add section 1.2, select Section 1.1 and choose Add After.

Questions

To edit the first question to a testbank, double-click on the first question entry displayed beneath the lowest level header. This will open the Question Editor. Choose the question type, then enter the question components.

To add another question to the testbank, select the first question and click the Add button on the Main window or choose Add After (or Add Before) from the Edit menu. The Question Editor will open so that you can type a new question. Continue to add questions under the same section heading or add more headings where additional questions can be added to the testbank.

USING THE SPELL CHECKER

Once you have created a new testbank, you can clean up any typographical errors you may have made using the built-in spell checker. On the Tools menu in the Main window, choose Spell. Choose whether you want to check the entire testbank or a selected section. The Options button allows you to select which components of the testbank you'd like to check: questions, answers, instructions, etc.

Click the Start button to begin looking for spelling mistakes. Any misspelled words will appear and suggestions for the correct spelling may appear. Single click on any of the suggestions to place it in the Change To area and click the Replace button to replace the misspelled word. If there is a word that is spelled correctly but the spell checker does not recognize it, click the Learn button to add the word to a user-defined dictionary.

Importing and Exporting Files

This section gives instruction on how to import files to use with the TestWorks program and how to export TestWorks testbank files.

IMPORTING TESTBANK FILES

Coded files from existing testbanks, such as exported data from TestMaster packages, can be converted into testbanks in that are compatible with TestWorks. The files must be text files that are specially set up chapter-by-chapter to fit into the new program's structure.

Coding Your Word Processing File

You will need to create a file for each chapter of testbank questions. Every question in the chapter must contain codes and information for TYPE, NUM, QUE, ANS, and END. Other codes and information are optional. Each of the codes is explained below.

.TYPE   The .TYPE code must begin each new question. On the line after the .TYPE code, enter either MC, TF, SA, ES, MA or BI to identify the type of question you are defining.

.NUM   The .NUM code must follow the .TYPE information. The number you type on the line after the .NUM code will be the item number of the question in the TestWorks testbank. Two questions of the same type in the same testbank cannot have the same item number.

.INS   (Optional) Type the .INS code on the line that precedes the Instructions for a question. You only need to use the Instruction code if you have specific directions for a question or a group of questions that would link several questions together. If the same instruction applies to more than one question, be sure to use the .INS code and copy the Instructions exactly for each question. The text you type after the .INS code will be placed in the Instructions field in the TestWorks testbank.

.PAGE   (Optional) On the line after the .PAGE code, type the numbers of the pages in your text where the answer to the question can be found.

.FIG   (Optional) On the line after the .FIG code, enter the Figure Code for the question if it refers to a specific figure. The Figure Code will indicate where you will import a graphics file. If more than one question refers to the same figure, be sure that the Figure Code you enter for each question is identical.

.BLANK   (Optional) On the line after the .BLANK code, enter a number from 1 to 50 to indicate the number of blank lines that should be left on a printed test if you choose to have the answer blanks printed on the test. This value will be used in the Workspace descriptor field.

.DIFF	(Optional) On the line after the .DIFF code, enter a number from 1 to 9 to indicate the difficulty level of the question.
.TOPIC	(Optional) On the line after the .TOPIC code, enter the topic of the question.
.SKILL	(Optional) On the line after the .SKILL code, enter the skill the question tests.
.OBJ	(Optional) On the line after the .OBJ code, enter the objective of the question.
.OTH1	(Optional) On the line after the .OTH1 code, enter additional descriptor information you define (for example, a key word in the question).
.OTH2	(Optional) On the line after the .OTH2 code, enter additional descriptor information you define.
.QUE	The .QUE, .ANS, and .END codes must be the last elements of each coded question. On the line after the .QUE code, enter the text of the question. For matching questions, type the text for Column 1 of the matching exercise.
.A, .B, ...	If you are defining a multiple-choice question, use the codes .A, .B, .C, .D, and .E to precede each of the answer choices. You can define up to five answer choices for each multiple-choice question.
F	If you are defining a multiple-choice question and want to freeze the order of any of the answer choices, type an F and a blank space before the text of the answer choice, as illustrated in the previous example with answer choice E. When you freeze the position of an answer choice, it will retain its position in the list of choices and will not be shuffled with the other answer choices when the question is printed on a test. This is useful for answer choices such as "none of the above," "all of the above," or "both a and c." In the last case, all answer choices should be preceded by an F. This answer will have a locked icon to the left of it in the Question Editor.
.FOIL	If you are defining a matching question, you can add an extra choice to Column 2 of the matching exercise by using the .FOIL code. On the line after the .FOIL code, type the text you want to appear in Column 2. This text should not be the correct answer.
.ANS	On the line after the .ANS code, type the answer for the question. For multiple-choice or bimodal questions, type a letter from A to E. For true/false questions, type T or F. For short-answer or essay questions, type the complete answer. For matching questions, type the correct answer that should appear in Column 2 of the matching exercise.
.END	The .END code must be the last code you type for any question and must exist on a line by itself.

The diagram below shows what a typical multiple-choice question would look like in a coded word-processing file. The multiple-choice question is item number 1 in the item bank. It relates to the topic "Representing data," is discussed on pages 32–33 of a reference source, and has five answer choices. The correct answer is A. The letter F that begins answer choice E indicates that this answer choice will remain fixed in order and will not be shuffled with the other answer choices when the question is printed on a test.

```
.TYPE
MC
.NUM
1
.TOPIC
Representing data
.PAGE
32-33
.QUE
Which type of graph is best for representing the change in the population of
deer over a ten year period?
.A
Line graph
.B
Circle graph
.C
Bar graph
.D
Pictograph
.E
F None of the above
.ANS
A
.END
```

Notice that in the preceding example each code is typed at the left margin on a line by itself and begins with a period (.). On the line following each code, text begins at the left margin. A blank line precedes the .TYPE code and a blank line follows the .END code.

Saving the Coded Word-Processing File

After you have entered the codes in your word-processing file, save the document as a text document in ASCII format. If your word processor gives you a choice, save the document without formatting commands or carriage returns.

For ease in identifying the file on your disk, you might want to use a naming scheme that identifies the chapter name and the file type. For example, if you have created a word-processing file of questions for Chapter 1, you might name the ASCII file CHAP01.ASC or CHAP01.TXT. In some cases, your word-processing software may automatically add a file extension to the filename. You will need to know the filename and extension when you run the TestWorks program and want to import the file.

Instructions for Importing Coded Files

Once you have a chapter of questions in coded text format that you are ready to import, start TestWorks and create a new testbank structure by choosing New Book on the File menu. Choose the appropriate number of levels of organization for the book (usually 2 or 3). Next, assign the testbank name and book abbreviation, name and describe each organizational level, and assign default styles for various parts of the testbank. See the "Creating a New Testbank" chapter of this Guide for more information about creating a new testbank.

A new book window will open, containing a dummy chapter 1. Keep this dummy chapter until you have imported one chapter of data. To do this, make sure chapter 1 is selected. Choose Import After on the File menu. You will see a dialog where you will choose the coded text file that you want to import. Once you make your choice and the file has been imported, you will see it as Chapter 2 in the book window. At this point, you may select the dummy chapter 1 and delete it by choosing Delete on the Edit menu.

As a precautionary measure, exit and save the book and make a duplicate of it after each chapter you import.

EXPORTING TEST FILES

You may want to transfer the test questions you create in TestWorks to a text file that you can modify further in a word processing program.

Once you have a TestWorks test that you want to export, choose Export on the File menu of the Main window. A dialog will open where you can give the file a name and choose where you would like to save it.

(NOTE: When you export a file, you lose any special formatting and graphics.)

Technical Information & Troubleshooting

Problem When you run TestWorks, the text in some dialog boxes looks cropped or doesn't fit in the space provided.

Solution If you are running TestWorks under Windows 95, you can remedy this problem by selecting Control Panels—Display—Settings and decreasing the resolution to 640 x 480, or by changing the display from Large Fonts to Small Fonts.

Problem When you try to print a test or a testbank, nothing prints.

Solution If you are running TestWorks under Windows 95 and printing to a non-PostScript printer, you will need to do the following steps before printing:

1. On the Start menu, choose Settings, then Printers.
2. Highlight your printer and click the right mouse button.
3. Select Properties—Details—Spool Settings.
4. Change the Spool Data Format to RAW (not EMF).

Problem You forgot your password for TestWorks.

Solution Sorry, you cannot recover your old password, but you can do something that will let you enter a new one. If you have the Windows version of the program, you will need to delete the user preferences file (userpref.prf) from the directory containing the TestWorks program files. If you have the Macintosh version, delete the file (TGEQ Prefs). Then, restart the program and register a new password. *(NOTE: If you delete the user preferences file, you will also lose other settings you may have chosen.)*

Problem While you were using the Windows version of the program, you got a General Protection Violation error window.

Solution Click the Abort button then close the application. Reboot your machine and then restart TestWorks. Keep the file OIT.DBG that gets created, as it might be used to help Tech Support diagnose the error.

Appendix - Graphics Files

The Graphics folder that gets installed with TestWorks contains figures that you can insert into any question in a testbank or test. For information on how to import graphics and save them in the Graphics Library, see the "Inserting Graphics" section of this Guide.

The abbreviated names of the graphic files inside the Graphics folder are descriptive of their contents. The two digits at the end of each filename indicate the approximate width of the graphic in number of characters. The following list provides a filename and brief description of each figure.

Category: ANGLES

ANS15.29	A 15-degree angle in standard position
ANS25.26	A 25-degree angle in standard position
ANS30.21	A 30-degree angle in standard position
ANS40.20	A 40-degree angle in standard position
ANS50.16	A 50-degree angle in standard position
ANS80.20	A 80-degree angle in standard position
ANS90.14	A 90-degree angle in standard position
ANS100.25	A 100-degree angle in standard position
ANS115.19	A 115-degree angle in standard position
ANS120.19	A 120-degree angle in standard position
ANS140.34	A 140-degree angle in standard position
AN20.22	A 20-degree angle not in standard position
AN45.19	A 45-degree angle not in standard position
AN50.22	A 50-degree angle not in standard position
AN65.10	A 65-degree angle not in standard position
AN70.12	A 70-degree angle not in standard position
AN90.11	A 90-degree angle not in standard position
AN105.34	A 105-degree angle not in standard position
AN120.17	A 120-degree angle not in standard position
AN155.34	A 155-degree angle not in standard position

Category: CIRCLES

CIRCLEA.17	A circle with diameter, radius and chord
CIRCLEB.17	A circle with two diameters and two chords
CIRCLEC.15	A labeled circle with two diameters and two chords
CIRCLED.12	A labeled circle with two radii and four chords
DIAMHOR.13	A circle with one horizontal diameter
DIAMLEFT.12	A circle with one diameter sloping up to the left
DIAMRT.12	A circle with one diameter sloping up to the right
RAD3.12	A circle with a radius drawn to the 3 o'clock position
RAD9.12	A circle with a radius drawn to the 9 o'clock position
RAD12.12	A circle with a radius drawn to the 12 o'clock position
UNCIRC1.31	A unit circle with points marked on circle
UNCIRC2.31	A unit circle with angles and directional arrows

Category: GRAPHS

BARGR1.34	A bar graph with bars at four levels
BARGR2.34	Another bar graph with bars at four levels

Category: LINES

HORLINE.34	Horizontal line
INTLINEA.16	Pair of intersecting lines
INTLINEB.14	Another pair of intersecting lines
INTLINEC.16	Another pair of intersecting lines
INTLINED.11	Another pair of intersecting lines
NUMLIN6.27	Number line with six tick marks, no scale
NUMLIN7.31	Number line with scale from -7 to 7
NUMLIN9.29	Number line with 9 equally spaced points, no scale
NUMLIN15.33	Number line with 15 tick marks, no scale
PARLINEH.26	Pair of horizontal parallel lines
PARLINEV.8	Pair of vertical parallel lines
PARLINED.14	Pair of slanted parallel lines
PERPLINA.12	Labeled vertical line met by a ray at right angles
PERPLINB.16	Pair of unlabeled perpendicular lines

Category: QUADRIL

PARALLA.18	A parallelogram
PARALLB.24	Another parallelogram
PARALTA.17	A parallelogram with an interior altitude
PARALTB.9	A parallelogram with an exterior altitude
RECTHA.12	A rectangle in horizontal position
RECTHB.20	Another rectangle in horizontal position
RECTHC.14	Another rectangle in horizontal position
RECTVA.6	A rectangle in vertical position
RECTVB.9	Another rectangle in vertical position
SQDIAG.8	A square with one diagonal
SQUAREA.7	A small square
SQUAREB.10	A larger square
TRAPA.15	A trapezoid
TRAPB.15	A trapezoid with the altitude

Category: SOLIDS

CUBE1.13	A cube
CUBE2.13	A cube with a different view
CYLIND1.12	A cylinder with radius
CYLIND2.18	A cylinder on its side with radius
CYLIND3.12	Another cylinder with radius
CYLIND4.15	A cylinder with diameter
CYLIND5.16	A cylinder with diameter and center
PYRAMID1.13	A pyramid
PYRAMID2.17	Another pyramid
RECTPR1.13	A rectangular prism
RECTPR2.14	Another rectangular prism
RECTPR3.14	Another rectangular prism
RECTPR4.18	Another rectangular prism
RECTPR5.21	Still another rectangular prism
TRIPR1.19	A triangular prism with right angles

Category: TRIANGLE

ACUALTA.23	An acute triangle with altitude drawn in
ACUALTB.21	Another acute triangle with altitude drawn in
ACUTEA.19	An acute triangle
ACUTEB.19	Another acute triangle
ACUTEC.16	Still another acute triangle
EQUILAT.10	An equilateral triangle
ISOSA.13	An isosceles triangle
ISOSB.11	Another isosceles triangle
ISOSC.10	Still another isosceles triangle
RIGHTA.7	A right triangle
RIGHTB.7	Another right triangle
RIGHTC.16	Another right triangle
RIGHTD.16	Another right triangle
RIGHTE.19	Still another right triangle

Limited Warranty

The CD-ROM included in this package is warranted against defects in materials and workmanship for a period of 90 days from your receipt of this CD-ROM. This limited warranty is void if the CD-ROM is damaged by causes not arising from defects in materials or construction. Addison Wesley Longman does not warrant that the program on the CD-ROM will be free from error or will meet your specific requirements. Further, Addison Wesley Longman makes the program available on an "As Is" basis, with no express or implied warranty concerning the program's fitness for a particular purpose.

In no event shall Addison Wesley Longman be liable to anyone for special, collateral, incidental, or consequential damages in connection with or arising from the purchase or use of the program. The sole and exclusive liability shall not exceed the purchase price of the CD-ROM. Addison Wesley Longman shall not be liable for any claim of any kind whatsoever by any other party against the user of the program. Some states do not allow the exclusion or limitation of implied warranties or consequential damages, so the above limitations or exclusions may not apply to you in those states.

During the 90-day warranty period, defective CD-ROMs will be replaced when returned with proof of purchase/ownership and with return postage prepaid. The replacement CD-ROM will be warranted for 90 days from the date of replacement. Other than the postage requirement, no charge will be made for the replacement. Mail defective CD-ROMs to:

Scott Foresman - Addison Wesley Publishing Company
Electronic Media Technical Support
2725 Sand Hill Road
Menlo Park, CA 94025

For technical assistance call our toll-free customer service hotline: 1-800-227-1936 or 1-800-982-6140 (within California).

Correlations Between *Math Course 2* and Model Problems

Chapter 1   **Making Sense of the World of Data**

Bimodal	Dynamic	Static	Lesson	Objective
2	1–3		**1-1** Interpreting Graphs	Read and interpret bar graphs. Read and interpret circle graphs.
1, 5	1, 2, 4, 5	3	**1-2** Making Bar Graphs	Create a bar graph from a table of data. Create a double-bar graph.
1, 3, 5, 6	1–3, 5, 6	4	**1-3** Line Plots and Stem-and-Leaf Diagrams	Make a line plot. Make a stem-and-leaf diagram.
1–5, 8, 11	1–11		**1-4** Mean, Median, Mode, and Range	Find the mean, median, mode, and range for a set of data. Decide if the mean, median, or mode best summarizes a set of data.
1, 2, 4, 8	1, 2, 4	3, 5–8	**1-5** Line Graphs	Read and interpret line graphs. Recognize trends.
1–3	1–3	4–7	**1-6** Scatterplots and Relationships	Read and interpret scatterplots. Make scatterplots. Recognize relationships in data.
3, 5	2	1, 3–5	**1-7** Trend Lines	Construct trend lines. Use trend lines to make predictions.

Chapter 2   The Language of Algebra: Formulas, Expressions, and Equations

Bimodal	Dynamic	Static	Lesson	Objective
1–3, 6, 8, 9	1–5, 7–10	6	**2-1** Formulas and Variables	Use formulas to show relationships among quantities. Use variables to represent quantities. Substitute values for variables.
1	2–4	1, 5–7	**2-2** Order of Operations	Use the order of operations to find the values of expressions. Use the associative, commutative, and distributive properties.
5, 6	2–5, 7	1, 6	**2-3** Formulas and Tables	Use a formula to make a table of values. Find a formula when given a table of values.
2–4	1–4		**2-4** Inverse Operations	Use inverse operations.
1, 2, 5–8	1, 2, 4, 5, 7, 8	3, 6	**2-5** Translating Words to Expressions	Translate words and phrases into algebraic expressions. Translate algebraic expressions into words and phrases.
1–3	2–4	1	**2-6** Solving Addition and Subtraction Equations	Solve addition and subtraction equations using inverse operations.
2, 3	2	1, 3, 4	**2-7** Solving Multiplication and Division Equations	Solve multiplication and division equations using inverse operations.
3	2, 4	1, 3	**2-8** Problem Solving with Two-Step Equations	Use more than one inverse operation to solve an equation.

Chapter 3 Number Sense: Decimals and Fractions

Bimodal	Dynamic	Static	Lesson	Objective
	1–3		**3-1** Place Value: Comparing and Ordering Decimals	Compare and order decimals.
1, 2, 4, 5, 7, 8	1, 2, 4–8	3, 9	**3-2** Estimating by Rounding	Round to the nearest place. Round to whole numbers to estimate. Use front-end estimation and compatible numbers to estimate.
1, 2	1–3		**3-3** Problem Solving: Sums and Differences of Decimals	Solve addition and subtraction equations containing decimals.
1–6	1, 2, 4, 5	3, 6	**3-4** Problem Solving: Products and Quotients of Decimals	Multiply and divide decimal numbers. Solve multiplication and division equations containing decimals.
1, 4–6	1–6		**3-5** Powers of 10 and Scientific Notation	Use exponents to write powers of 10. Write large numbers in scientific notation.
4–6	1, 4–6	2, 3	**3-6** Divisibility and Prime Factorization	Test for divisibility. Write any number as a product of primes.
1–6	1, 3, 4	2, 5, 6	**3-7** GCF and LCM	Find the greatest common factor of a pair of numbers. Find the least common multiple of a pair of numbers.
4	1, 3, 5, 6	2, 4	**3-8** Equivalent Fractions and Lowest Terms	Write equivalent fractions. Rewrite fractions in lowest terms.
1, 5	3, 4, 6	1, 2, 5	**3-9** Comparing and Ordering Fractions	Compare the values of fractions. Order fractions.
1, 2, 4, 5	3, 6	1, 2, 4, 5	**3-10** Converting Between Fractions and Decimals	Convert fractions to decimals. Convert decimals to fractions.

Chapter 4 Operations with Fractions

Bimodal	Dynamic	Static	Lesson	Objective
1–5	1–7		**4-1** Estimating: Fractions and Mixed Numbers	Estimate solutions to problems involving fractions.
1, 3, 4, 7–11, 13	1, 2, 4–6, 8, 10, 12, 14	3, 7, 9, 11, 13	**4-2** Adding and Subtracting Fractions	Find sums and differences of fractions. Solve equations involving fractions.
1–5, 8, 9	1–4, 7, 10, 12–14	5, 6, 8, 9, 11	**4-3** Adding and Subtracting Mixed Numbers	Find sums and differences of mixed numbers. Solve equations involving mixed numbers.
3, 4	1, 3, 5, 6	2, 4, 7	**4-4** Multiplying Fractions	Multiply fractions.
1, 6	2, 4, 5, 7	1, 3, 6	**4-5** Multiplying Mixed Numbers	Multiply mixed numbers.
2, 3	1, 4, 6	2, 3, 5, 7	**4-6** Dividing Fractions and Mixed Numbers	Divide fractions and mixed numbers.

Chapter 5 Geometry and Measurement

Bimodal	Dynamic	Static	Lesson	Objective
3–6	1–6		**5-1** Angles	Name angles. Measure angles.
1, 2, 4	2, 6	1, 3–5	**5-2** Parallel and Perpendicular Lines	Recognize parallel lines and their properties. Recognize perpendicular lines and their properties.
1, 2, 5, 6, 8	1–3, 6–9	4, 5	**5-3** Triangles and Quadrilaterals	Name and classify triangles. Name and classify quadrilaterals. Find the measures of angles in these figures.
4, 5	1, 2, 4, 5	3, 6	**5-4** Polygons	Classify polygons. Find the angle sums of polygons.
1, 2	1–3		**5-5** Perimeter and Area	Examine the relationship between perimeter and area.
1, 2, 4, 5	1–4, 6	5	**5-6** Squares and Square Roots	Find the side of a square when you know its area. Find a square root.
1, 6	3, 4, 6	1, 2, 5	**5-7** The Pythagorean Theorem	Use the special relationship among the sides of a right triangle. Use the Pythagorean Theorem.
1	1, 2	3	**5-8** Areas of Triangles	Find the area of a triangle.
1, 5	1, 3, 4	2, 5, 6	**5-9** Areas of Parallelograms and Trapezoids	Find the area of a parallelogram. Find the area of a trapezoid.
1	2	1, 3	**5-10** Problem Solving: Areas of Irregular Figures	Find the areas of irregular shapes.

Chapter 6   **Ratios, Rates, and Proportions**

Bimodal	Dynamic	Static	Lesson	Objective
2, 3, 6–10	1–8	9, 10	**6-1** Exploring and Estimating Ratios	Identify ratios. Compare quantities using division.
	1–3, 6–10	4, 5	**6-2** Exploring and Estimating Rates	Compare two quantities with different units of measure. Make comparisons to one unit.
1	1, 3, 4	2	**6-3** Equivalent Ratios and Rates	Find equivalent ratios and rates.
2, 3	3–5	1, 2	**6-4** Using Tables to Explore Ratios and Rates	Use a table to find equivalent ratios and rates.
	3, 4	1, 2	**6-5** Creating Proportions	Use equivalent ratios to write proportions.
1, 2	3, 4	1, 2, 5	**6-6** Testing for Proportionality	Recognize proportional relationships.
1, 2	3, 4	1, 2	**6-7** Solving Proportions Using Unit Rates	Use unit rates to solve a proportion.
2, 4	1, 2, 6, 7	3–5	**6-8** Cross Multiplication	Use cross multiplication to solve a proportion. Use cross multiplication to check whether two ratios form a proportion.

Chapter 7 Proportion, Scale, and Similarity

Bimodal	Dynamic	Static	Lesson	Objective
1, 2, 4–6	1–6		**7-1** Measurement: Estimating Actual and Scale Distances	Read and understand scales. Estimate distances from maps using scales.
1, 2	1–3		**7-2** Calculating with Scales	Use scales and scale drawings to calculate actual distances.
1–3	1–3		**7-3** Problem Solving Using Maps	Use scales to read maps and make decisions.
1, 2	1, 2	3	**7-4** Creating Scale Drawings and Scale Models	Select a reasonable scale for a drawing, map, or model.
1, 4, 5	3–6	1, 2	**7-5** Choosing Appropriate Rates and Units	Select an appropriate scale for a particular situation. Write reciprocal rates that have the same meaning.
1, 2	2, 3	1	**7-6** Converting Units	Convert measurements from one unit to another.
2	1, 3	2	**7-7** Problem Solving: Converting Rates	Solve problems involving conversion of rates.
1	1, 3	2, 4	**7-8** Creating and Exploring Similar Figures	Identify similar figures. Write similarity statements.
1, 4	2, 4	1, 3, 5, 6	**7-9** Finding Measures of Similar Figures	Find missing side lengths in similar figures. Use shadows to find the heights of tall objects.
2	1	2–4	**7-10** Perimeters and Areas of Similar Figures	Use the scale factor to find perimeters and areas of similar figures.

Chapter 8   **Percents**

Bimodal	Dynamic	Static	Lesson	Objective
1, 2, 4	1, 2, 5	3–4	**8-1** Understanding Percents	Compare quantities by using percents.
1, 2, 4, 5, 7	1–7		**8-2** Linking Fractions, Decimals, and Percents	Understand the relationships between percents, fractions, and decimals.
5, 9	1–4, 6–9	5	**8-3** Percents Greater than 100 or Less than 1	Use percents that are less than 1%. Use percents that are greater than 100%.
	1–6		**8-4** Finding a Percent of a Number Mentally	Use mental math to find a percent of a number.
1–4	5–7	1–4	**8-5** Using Equations to Solve Percent Problems	Use equations to solve problems involving percents.
3–5, 7	1, 2	3–7	**8-6** Solving Percent Problems with Proportions	Use proportions to solve percent problems.
1	2–4	1, 5–7	**8-7** Problem Solving: Percent Increase and Decrease	Solve problems involving percent increase and percent decrease.

Chapter 9   **Integers**

Bimodal	Dynamic	Static	Lesson	Objective
3–5, 8, 10–12, 14–19	1–6, 8, 9, 11, 12, 14–22	7, 10, 13, 23	**9-1** Using Integers to Represent Quantities	Use integers to represent real-world quantities. Find the opposite of an integer. Find the absolute value of an integer.
6, 7	1–4, 6, 7	5	**9-2** Comparing and Ordering Integers	Compare and order integers.
1–3	1, 2	3–7	**9-3** The Coordinate Plane	Graph points on a coordinate plane.
2, 5, 6	1–4	5–8	**9-4** Adding Integers	Add integers.
1, 3–5	1–4	5–7	**9-5** Subtracting Integers	Subtract integers.
1–3, 5	1–4	5–8	**9-6** Multiplying Integers	Multiply integers.
1, 2, 4, 5	1–3	4–7	**9-7** Dividing Integers	Divide integers.

Chapter 10 The Patterns of Algebra: Equations and Graphs

Bimodal	Dynamic	Static	Lesson	Objective
2	1, 3	2	**10-1** Quantities, Constants, and Variables	Identify variables and constants.
	2, 4	1, 3, 5, 6	**10-2** Relating Graphs to Stories	Match a graph to a story. Write a story for a graph.
1, 2, 4	1, 2, 4–6	3	**10-3** Tables and Expressions	Write rules for sequences. Identify arithmetic and geometric sequences.
1–3	1–3		**10-4** Understanding and Writing Equations	Write an equation from a table of values.
	1	2–4	**10-5** Equations and Graphs	Draw the graph of an equation.
1–3	1, 2	3	**10-6** Solving Equations Using Tables	Use tables to solve equations.
1, 2	3	1, 2	**10-7** Solving Equations Using Graphs	Use graphs to solve equations.
5, 6	1, 5	2–4, 6	**10-8** Relating Equations and Inequalities	Graph inequalities on a number line. Write the inequality represented by a graph.
1–3	1–4		**10-9** Integer Addition and Subtraction Equations	Solve addition and subtraction equations involving positive and negative integers.
1–3	1–4		**10-10** Integer Multiplication and Division Equations	Solve multiplication and division problems involving positive and negative integers.
1	2–4	1	**10-11** Solving Two-Step Equations	Solve two-step equations involving positive and negative integers.
1, 3	1, 2	3	**10-12** Problem Solving with Integer Equations	Solve real-world problems by using integer equations.

Chapter 11　**Geometry: Solids, Circles, and Transformations**

Bimodal	Dynamic	Static	Lesson	Objective
1–3	2–5	1, 6	**11-1** Exploring Polyhedrons	Name polyhedrons. Sketch polyhedrons.
1, 5–8	2, 4–8	1, 3, 9	**11-2** Isometric and Orthographic Drawing	Match isometric and orthographic views. Draw front, side, and top views of a solid. Draw a figure in perspective from its front, top, and side views.
1–3	1–3		**11-3** Polyhedron Nets and Surface Areas	Find the surface area of a polyhedron.
1–3	1–3		**11-4** Volumes of Prisms	Find the volume of a prism.
1–3	1–3		**11-5** Circles and Circle Graphs	Make circle graphs.
2–6	2, 4–6	1, 3	**11-6** Pi and Circumference	Learn the meaning of π. Find the circumference of a circle.
1, 2	1–3		**11-7** Area of a Circle	Find the area of a circle.
1, 2	1–3		**11-8** Surface Areas of Cylinders	Find the surface area of a cylinder.
1, 2	1–3		**11-9** Volumes of Cylinders	Find the volume of a cylinder.
1	1–6		**11-10** Translations	Draw translations on a coordinate plane. Write rules for translations.
		1–6	**11-11** Reflections and Line Symmetry	Identify lines of symmetry. Reflect figures on a coordinate plane.
4	1	2–9	**11-12** Rotations and Rotational Symmetry	Identify figures with rotational symmetry. Determine how far a figure has been rotated. Rotate figures on a coordinate plane.

Chapter 12   **Counting and Probability**

Bimodal	Dynamic	Static	Lesson	Objective
1–3	1–4		**12-1** Counting Methods	Use tree diagrams and the Counting Principle to find all the outcomes for a set of choices.
1, 3–5, 7 9	1–3, 5, 6, 8, 9	4, 7	**12-2** Arrangements	Count the number of ways items can be arranged. Use factorial products to count arrangements.
1, 2, 4	1–5		**12-3** Choosing a Group	Calculate the number of ways to choose some items out of a larger group when the order is unimportant.
1–3	1, 2	3, 4	**12-4** Odds and Fairness	Find the odds that an event happens.
1–3, 5	1–5		**12-5** Probability	Find the probability of an event.
4–6	1–3, 7	4–6, 8, 9	**12-6** Experimental Probability	Use experimental probability to estimate probabilities. Find probabilities involving geometric figures.
6, 7	1, 5	2–4, 6–9	**12-7** Independent and Dependent Events	Decide whether two events are dependent or independent. Find probabilities of dependent and independent events.

Model Testbank Items

Chapter 1 Making Sense of the World of Data

Section 1A Communicating with Data

1-1 Interpreting Graphs

1) Use the bar graph.

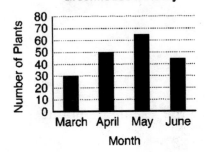

a. During which month were 50 plants sold? _____

b. How many plants were sold from April through May?
____

2)

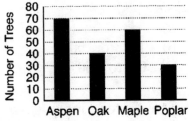

How many Maple trees are at Mountainside Park?
A) 70   B) 30   C) 50   D) 60

3) Use the circle graph.

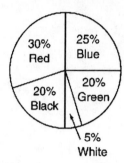

Aprons Sold at Bazaar by Color

a. What two colors occur in the same amount?

_____

b. Which two colors together make up 55% of the sales? _____

c. Which two colors together make up more than half of the aprons sold? _____

1–2 Making Bar Graphs

1) What is a convenient scale to use for making a bar graph of the data 3, 7, 6, 2, 4?

A) 0 to 100   B) 10 to 50
C) 0 to 10   D) 0 to 50

2) Which is a convenient scale to use for making a bar graph of the data 485, 263, 396, 180?

A) 5   B) 10   C) 50   D) 1

3) Make a double-bar graph for the number of elk and deer in the state park.

Blue Geyser State Park				
Year	1960	1970	1980	1990
Elk	91	86	79	72
Deer	62	73	85	90

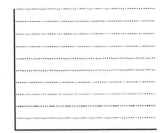

4) Use the double-bar graph.

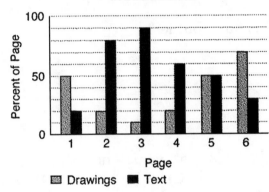

a. Which page has the least amount of drawings on it? _____

b. Which are the only pages that might possibly also have bird photographs on them? _____

5) What is a convenient interval to use for making a bar graph of the data 2,500, 8,600, 3,700, 4,200?

A) 1   B) 100   C) 1,000   D) 10

1-3   Line Plots and Stem-and-Leaf Diagrams

1)   Use the line plot.

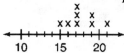

How many data points have a value of 16?

A) 0   B) 1   C) 3   D) 2

2)   Use the line plot.

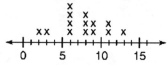

a. How many data points have a value of 19? ____

b. Which data value is an outlier? ____

3)   Use the line plot.

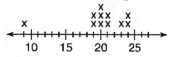

How many data points have a value of 6?

A) 4   B) 0   C) 1   D) 2

4)   Use the stem-and-leaf diagram of ages of a group of veterans.

Stem	Leaf
9	4 5
8	2 6 9 9
7	0 1 3 5 5 9
6	5 8

What was the age of the oldest veteran in the group?

5) Use the stem–and–leaf diagram of the ages of people rollerblading in the park.

Stem	Leaf
4	2
3	1 4
2	0 2 3 6
1	2 3 3 4 4 4 5

How many people are 14 years old?
A) 0   B) 1   C) 3   D) 2

6) Use the stem–and–leaf diagram of book report scores.

Stem	Leaf
9	0 2 4 4 5
8	1 1 3 5 6 6 9 9
7	2 2 2 5 8 8
6	9 9

How many students earned scores in the 80s or 90s?
A) 7   B) 8   C) 13   D) 14

1-4 Mean, Median, Mode, and Range

1) What is the median of the set of data 21, 24, 18, 35, 12?
A) 21   B) 12   C) 18   D) 17

2) What is the mode(s) for the data 2, 4, 1, 3, 2, 1, 2?
A) 4   B) 2   C) 1   D) 3

3) What is the mean for the data 15, 3, 24, 11, 29, 2?
A) 11   B) 13   C) 12   D) 14

4) What is the range of the data 73, 82, 71, 89?
A) 12   B) 8   C) 18   D) 16

5) What is the median of the set of data 88, 92, 96, 97?
A) 92   B) 82   C) 88   D) 94

6) Which measure of central tendency best summarizes these data?

     3, 58, 62, 54, 55, 61, 60

A) Mode   B) Median   C) Mean   D) Range

7) Which measure of central tendency best summarizes these data?

        Heights in cm of plants after one month :
        24, 21, 18, 22, 19, 23, 8, 5

A) Median   B) Mean
C) Mode   D) Not here

8) Find the mean of the data:
        82, 84, 90, 92?

A) 84   B) 85   C) 87   D) 86

9) Find the median of the data:
        80, 90, 86, 92

10) Find the mode of the data:
        63, 62, 65, 61

11) Find the range of the data:
        28, 35, 29, 32?

A) 7   B) 12   C) 9   D) 11

Section 1B Trends and Relationships in Data

1–5 Line Graphs

1) Use the line graph.

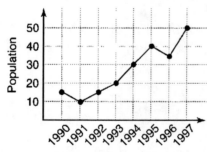

Wolf Population in Far North Park

What was the wolf population in 1995?

A) 10   B) 20   C) 30   D) 40

2)   Use the line graph.

Bear Population on Glacier Island

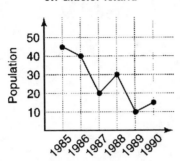

In what year was the bear population 30 bears?
A) 1982   B) 1989   C) 1988   D) 1987

3)   Use the line graph.

Soccer Teams in Midvale

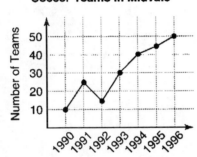

In what time period did the number of teams decrease?

4)   Use the line graph.

Number of Pine Trees in Valley Park

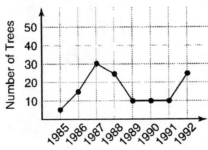

What was the trend in the number of pine trees from 1988 to 1990?
A) Increasing   B) No trend
C) Decreasing   D) Holding steady

5) Use the line graph.

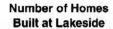

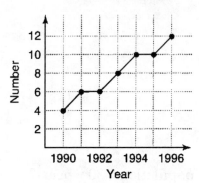

Does the graph show an increasing or decreasing trend, or neither?

6) Use the line graph.

Growth of Alpine Recreation Center by Number of Members

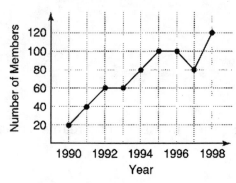

During what years was there no increase in the number of members?

7) Use the line graph.

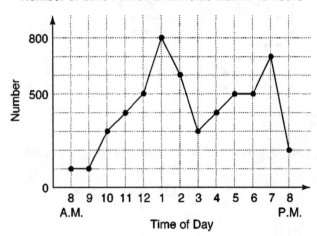

Number of Cars Parked at Elmside Mall in 12 hours

At what time of day were the most cars parked at Elmside Mall?

8) Use the scatter plots.

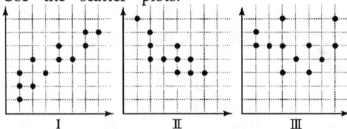

I   II   III

For which scatter plot would a trend line predict higher values in the future?

A) I   B) III
C) II   D) Not here

1-6 Scatterplots and Relationships

1) Use the scatter plots.

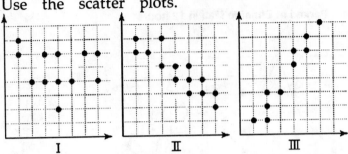

I   II   III

Which scatter plot shows a no relationship relationship?
A) II   B) III
C) I   D) Not here

2) Use the scatter plot.

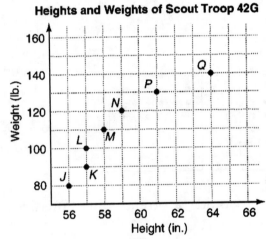

Heights and Weights of Scout Troop 42G

Which point was plotted for 57 in., 90 lb?
A) M   B) K   C) L   D) N

3) Use the scatter plots.

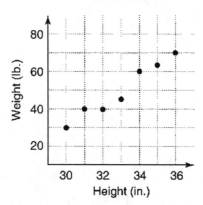

Heights and Weights of Brian's Pets

What is the interval on the horizontal scale?

A) 2 in.   B) 10 lb   C) 1 in.   D) 5 lb

4) Use the scatter plot.

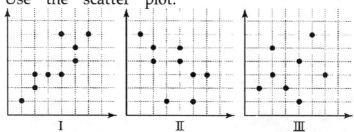

I   II   III

Which scatter plot shows no relationship?

5) Create a scatter plot for the number of robins nesting in Oak Park.

Year	1960	1970	1980	1990
Number	24	38	45	59

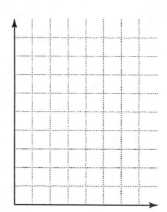

6)   Use   the   scatter   plot.

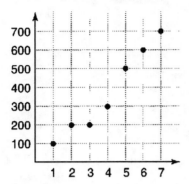

**Weekly Attendance at
Trout Lake State Park**

Is   there   a   relationship   in   the   data?   If   so,   is   it   positive
or   negative?

7)   Use   the   scatter   plot.

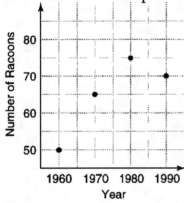

What   is   the   greatest   value   in   the   scatter   plot?

1-7   Trend Lines

1)   Use the scatter plot.

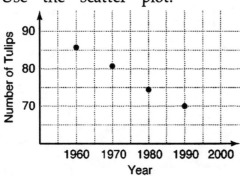

Draw a trend line for the scatterplot. Which prediction for the number of tulips in the year 2000 is closest to the trend line?

A) 75   B) 70   C) 65   D) 60

2)   Use the scatter plot.

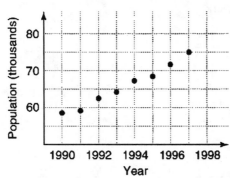

Which prediction of the population in 1998 is closest to the trend?

A) 78,000   B) 75,000   C) 88,000   D) 83,000

3) Use the scatter plot.

**Weekly Attendance at the
Seaside Community Theatre**

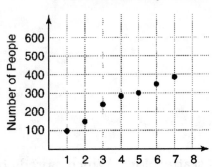

Which prediction for week 8 attendance is closest to the trend?

A) 420   B) 370   C) 500   D) 300

4) Use the scatter plot.

Deer Population In Grandview State Park

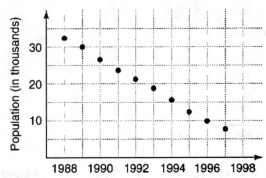

Draw a trend line.

5)   Use the scatter plot.

Height of Karl's Plant

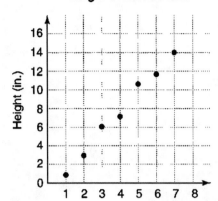

Which prediction for the height of Karl's plant in 8 months is closest to the trend?

A) 17 in.   B) 12 in.   C) 16 in.   D) 14 in.

Chapter 1 Making Sense of the World of Data

Section 1A Communicating with Data

1-1 Interpreting Graphs

1)   Answer: a. April
                 b. 115

2)   Answer: D

3)   Answer: a. Black and green
                 b. Red and blue
                 c. Red and blue

1-2 Making Bar Graphs

1)   Answer: C

2)   Answer: C

3)   Answer:
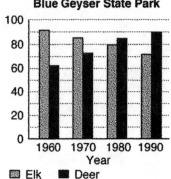

4)   Answer: a. 3
                 b. 1 and 4

5)   Answer: C

1-3 Line Plots and Stem-and-Leaf Diagrams

1)   Answer: B

2)   Answer: a. 2
                 b. 9

3)   Answer: A

4)   Answer: 95

5)   Answer: C

6)   Answer: C

1–4   Mean, Median, Mode, and Range

1)   Answer: A

2)   Answer: B

3)   Answer: D

4)   Answer: C

5)   Answer: D

6)   Answer: B

7)   Answer: A

8)   Answer: C

9)   Answer: 88

10)   Answer: No   mode

11)   Answer: A

Section 1B Trends and Relationships in Data
1–5   Line Graphs

1)   Answer: D

2)   Answer: C

3)   Answer: 1991 – 1992

4)   Answer: B

5)   Answer: Increasing

6)   Answer: 1992 – 1993, 1995 – 1996

7)   Answer: 1:00 pm

8)   Answer: A

1-6   Scatterplots and Relationships

1)   Answer: C

2)   Answer: B

3)   Answer: C

4)   Answer: III

5)   Answer: Possible   answer:

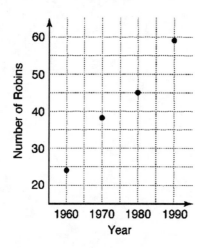

6)   Answer: Yes,   positive

7)   Answer: 75

1-7   Trend   Lines

1)   Answer: C

2)   Answer: A

3)   Answer: A

4) Answer:

Deer Population in Grandview State Park

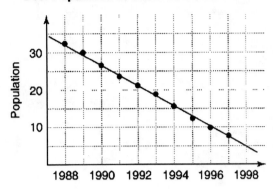

5) Answer: C

Chapter 2 The Language of Algebra: Formulas, Expressions...

Section 2A Formulas

2-1 Formulas and Variables

1) For m = 3, the formula x = 2m gives what value for x?

   A) 8 B) 12 C) 6 D) 5

2) For k = 7, the formula x = 8k gives what value for x?

   A) 7 B) 8 C) 1.1 D) 56

3) For b = 5, the formula x = 3(b + 6) gives what value for x?

   A) 23 B) 21 C) 33 D) 14

4) The formula for changing feet (f) to yards (y) is y = $\frac{f}{3}$. Evaluate the formula if f = 24.

5) The formula for changing minutes (m) to hours (h) is h = $\frac{m}{60}$. Evaluate the formula if m = 240.

6) Use c = 25h + m to find the cost (c) of having a fence built if the charges are $25 per hour (h) for labor plus the cost of materials (m). The builder estimates that it will requires 3 hours of labor and $95 for materials.

   A) $120 B) $170 C) $145 D) $360

7) Evaluate the formula x = $\frac{(a+b)}{4}$ for a = 8 and b = 16.

8) Evaluate the formula x = 4(s – 6) for s = 26.

   A) 80 B) 128 C) 104 D) 98

9)   For $r = 9$ and $t = 4$, the formula $x = \dfrac{(r+7)}{t}$ gives what value for x?

       A) 16   B) 3   C) 4   D) 13

10)   For $d = 5$, the formula $f = 2d - 2$ gives what value for f?

2–2   Order of Operations

1)   Which operation should be done first: $(16 + 4) \div 5$?

       A) –   B) ÷   C) +   D) ×

2)   Find the value of the expression $40 + 16 \div (9 - 7)$.

3)   Find the value of the expression $2(3 + 7) \div 5 + 6$.

4)   Insert parentheses to make the sentence true:

       $8 + 2 \div 5 = 2$

5)   Which equation shows the Associative Property?

       A) $7 + 3 = 2 \times 5$
       B) $8 + 6 = 6 + 8$
       C) $4 \times (3 \times 6) = 4 \times (6 \times 3)$
       D) $2 \times (4 \times 6) = (2 \times 4) \times 6$

6)   Which property is shown by $7 + 4 = 4 + 7$?

7)   Which property is shown by $3(6 + 2) = 3 \times 6 + 3 \times 2$?

2–3   Formulas and Tables

1)   Which is the table for $y = x - 4$?

A)

x	5	6	7	8	9
y	9	10	11	12	13

B)

x	1	2	3	4	5
y	4	8	12	16	20

C)

x	5	6	7	8	9
y	1	2	3	4	5

D)

x	1	2	3	4	5
y	5	6	7	8	9

2) Solve.

Carol is 6 years older than her brother Mark. Complete the table of values for the formula c = m + 6, where c is Carol's age and m is Mark's age.

m	5	6	7	8	9
c					

3) Which is the table of values for the formula y = x + 7?

A)

x	1	2	3	4	5
y	10	8	6	4	2

B)

x	1	2	3	4	5
y	8	9	10	11	12

C)

x	1	2	3	4	5
y	3	6	9	12	15

D)

x	1	2	3	4	5
y	4	8	12	16	20

4) Find a formula relating the variables.

x	12	13	14	15	16
y	9	10	11	12	13

5) What formula gives the values in this table?

x	1	2	3	4	5
y	6	12	18	24	30

A) y = 7x   B) y = 6x
C) y = x – 6   D) y = x + 7

6) What formula gives the values in this table?

x	10	20	30	40	50
y	5	10	15	20	25

A) $y = 2x$ B) $y = \dfrac{x}{2}$ C) $y = \dfrac{x}{5}$ D) $y = 5x$

7) Find a formula relating the variables.

x	8	9	10	11	12
y	12	13	14	15	16

Section 2B Expressions and Equations

2–4   Inverse Operations

1) Name the inverse operation of dividing by 7.

2) Solve.

The following operations are performed on a number: ×5, then +2. What operations must be performed to return to the original number?
A) ÷5, –2   B) +2, ×5   C) +5, ×2   D) –2, ÷5

3) Solve.

The following operations are performed on a number: +6, then ×7. What operations must be performed to return to the original number?
A) ×7, +6   B) ÷7, –6   C) –6, ×7   D) –6, ÷7

4) Solve.

The following operations are performed on a number: + 14, then ÷3. What operations must be performed to return to the original number?
A) +14, ×3   B) ×3, –14   C) ÷3, +14   D) –14, ÷3

2-5   Translating Words to Expressions

1) What algebraic expression expresses the product of 7 and h?

   A) $7 + h$ B) $7 - h$ C) $\dfrac{h}{7}$ D) $7h$

2) What algebraic expression expresses m divided by 2?

   A) $\dfrac{m}{2}$ B) $2m$ C) $\dfrac{2}{m}$ D) $m - 2$

3) Which algebraic expression best expresses double the difference of x and 3?

   A) $3 - 2x$ B) $2(x - 3)$
   C) $2x - 3$ D) $2(x + 3)$

4) Write an algebraic expression for twice the sum of a number r and 7.

5) Write a phrase for the algebraic expression $\dfrac{(d + 2)}{5}$.

   A) 2 more than d less than 5
   B) The sum of one fifth d and 2
   C) 2 more than d times 5
   D) One fifth the sum of d and 2

6) What phrase describes the algebraic expression $\dfrac{f}{3}$?

   A) One third of f   B) Triple the number f
   C) Product of f and 3   D) f times 3

7) What phrase best describes the algebraic expression $5\dfrac{k}{2}$?

   A) Product of 5, k, and 2
   B) Product of 5 and 2, divided by k
   C) 5 times half of k
   D) 5 times the difference of k and 2

8) What phrase describes the algebraic expression m - 2?
   A) Sum of m and 2   B) 2 less m
   C) m times 2   D) Difference of m and 2

2-6 Solving Addition and Subtraction Equations

1) What is the solution of the equation $59 = 8a + 3$?
   A) 8   B) 7   C) 6   D) 56

2) What number satisfies the equation $r - 17 = 402$?
   A) 384   B) 419   C) 420   D) 385

3) What number satisfies the equation $w - 29 = 65$?
   A) 92   B) 94   C) 1,885   D) 36

4) Solve the equation:
   $707 = 23 + s$.

2-7 Solving Multiplication and Division Equations

1) Which number satisfies the equation $36 = 4p$?
   A) 8   B) 140   C) 9   D) 144

2) Solve the equation:
   $$\frac{n}{6} = 17$$
   A) 85   B) 23   C) 102   D) 11

3) What value satisfies the equation $\frac{a}{8} = 32$?

   A) 256   B) 246   C) $\frac{1}{4}$ D) 4

4) Solve the equation $6b = 72$.

2-8 Problem Solving with Two-Step Equations

1) Solve the equation $6w - 5 = 43$.

2) Solve the equation $\frac{s}{3} + 8 = 13$.

3) What is the solution of the equation $8h + 6 = 350$?
   A) 244   B) 44   C) 43   D) 42

4)   Solve the equation $\dfrac{c}{6} - 5 = 12$.

Chapter 2 The Language of Algebra: Formulas, Expressions...

Section 2A Formulas

2-1 Formulas and Variables

1) Answer: C

2) Answer: D

3) Answer: C

4) Answer: 8

5) Answer: 4

6) Answer: B

7) Answer: 6

8) Answer: A

9) Answer: C

10) Answer: 8

2-2 Order of Operations

1) Answer: C

2) Answer: 48

3) Answer: 10

4) Answer: $(8 + 2) \div 5 = 2$

5) Answer: D

6) Answer: Commutative Property of Addition

7) Answer: Distributive property

2-3 Formulas and Tables

1) Answer: C

2)   Answer:

x	5	6	7	8	9
y	11	12	13	14	15

3)   Answer: B

4)   Answer: $y = x - 3$

5)   Answer: B

6)   Answer: B

7)   Answer: $y = x + 4$

Section 2B Expressions and Equations

2-4   Inverse Operations

1)   Answer: Multiplying by 7

2)   Answer: D

3)   Answer: B

4)   Answer: B

2-5   Translating Words to Expressions

1)   Answer: D

2)   Answer: A

3)   Answer: B

4)   Answer: $2(r + 7)$ or $2(8 + r)$

5)   Answer: D

6)   Answer: A

7)   Answer: C

8)   Answer: D

2-6   Solving Addition and Subtraction Equations

1)   Answer: B

2)   Answer: B

3)   Answer: B

4)   Answer: 684

2–7   Solving Multiplication and Division Equations

1)   Answer: C

2)   Answer: C

3)   Answer: A

4)   Answer: 12

2–8   Problem Solving with Two–Step Equations

1)   Answer: 8

2)   Answer: 15

3)   Answer: C

4)   Answer: 102

Chapter 3 Number Sense: Decimals and Fractions

Section 3A Decimal Concepts

3–1   Place Value: Comparing and Ordering Decimals

1)   Which of these numbers is the least?
      A) 8.34   B) 8.433   C) 8.343   D) 8.334

2)   Compare using > or <.
      0.148 ☐ 0.184

3)   Compare using > or <.
      0.74584 ☐ 0.75484

3–2   Estimating by Rounding

1)   What is 4.35 rounded to the nearest tenth?
      A) 4.39   B) 4.0   C) 4.4   D) 5.0

2)   What is 3.902 rounded to the nearest hundredth?
      A) 38.0   B) 3.90   C) 3.91   D) 39.0

3)   Round 2.407 to the nearest whole number, tenth, and hundredth.

4)   What is 13.4 rounded to the nearest whole number?
      A) 13.5   B) 13   C) 14   D) 13.4

5)   What is 0.12 rounded to the nearest whole number?
      A) 0.1   B) 0   C) 1   D) 0.88

6)   Which is the best estimate for 8.07 ÷ 2.75?
      A) 10   B) 7   C) 3   D) 9

7)   Using compatible numbers, what is the best estimate for
      50.1 – 17.37?
      A) 20   B) 25   C) 30   D) 40

8)   Which is the best estimate for 6,200 ÷ 73?
      A) 40   B) 90   C) 70   D) 150

9) Solve.
Kevin makes $5.25 per hour as a part-time cook. He worked 182.5 hours this year. Which is the best estimate of the amount of money he made (before taxes) for the year.

A) $1,200   B) $500   C) $900   D) $1,500

3-3   Problem Solving   Sums and Differences of Decimals

1) What is the solution to the equation
$0.937 = x - 0.6115$.

A) $x = 1.5485$ B) $x = 3.255$
C) $x = 15.485$ D) $x = 0.3255$

2) Solve $34.59 = x + 14.52$.

A) 491.1   B) 49.11   C) 200.7   D) 20.07

3) Solve $0.405 = x - 0.413$.

3-4   Problem Solving   Products and Quotients of Decimals

1) What is the product of 2.17 and 3.47?

A) 75.299   B) 7.5299   C) 0.75299   D) 0.075299

2) Find the quotient $760.8 \div 31.7$.

A) 24   B) 23   C) 21   D) 26

3) Solve.
Julie earned $363.78 for 42.3 hours of work. What was her hourly wage?

A) $86.00   B) $7.60   C) $8.60   D) $76.00

4) What value solves the equation $0.81 = \frac{c}{2}$?

A) 4.05   B) 16.2   C) 2.62   D) 1.62

5) Solve.
Olivia sold banners that cost $5.9 each. If she sold 14 banners at a bazaar, how much money did she make in sales?

A) $826.00   B) $83.60   C) $82.60   D) $8.26

6) Solve $3.8w = 9.88$ to the nearest tenth.

A) $w = 26$ B) $w = 0.3$
C) $w = 2.6$ D) $w = 0.26$

3-5   Powers of 10 and Scientific Notation

1) What is 1,000,000 written as a power of 10?
A) 10^7 B) 10^8 C) 10^6 D) 10^5

2) What number is equal to 10^8?
A) 1,000,000,000   B) 100,000,000

C) $\dfrac{1}{100,000,000}$ D) 10,000,000

3) Evaluate 10^7.

4) What is 356,000 in scientific notation?
A) 35.6×10^3 B) 3.56×10^5
C) 356×10^3 D) 356×10^4

5) What is 700,000,000 in scientific notation?
A) 7×10^8 B) 7×10^9
C) 0.7×10^{10} D) 70×10^9

6) Write 7,911 in scientific notation.

A) 79.11×10^3

B) 7.911×10^3

C) 791.1×10^3

D) 0.7911×10^3

Section 3B Fraction Concepts

3-6 Divisibility and Prime Factorization

1) Which number is divisible by 2, 5, and 9?

A) 520   B) 720   C) 400   D) 250

2) Which number is divisible 3, 4, and 6?

A) 378   B) 450   C) 486   D) 516

3) Test 693 for divisibility by 2, 3, 4, 5, 6, 7, 8, 9, and 10.

4) What is the prime factorization of 180?

A) $2 \times 3 \times 5^2$

B) $2^2 \times 3 \times 5$

C) $2^2 \times 3^2 \times 5$

D) $2^2 \times 3^2 \times 7$

5) What is the prime factorization of 315?

A) $3^2 \times 7^2$

B) $3^3 \times 5^2$

C) $3^2 \times 5 \times 7$

D) $3 \times 5^2 \times 7$

6) What is the prime factorization of 189?

A) $3 \times 7^2 \times 11$

B) $3^2 \times 5 \times 11$

C) $3^3 \times 5$

D) $3^3 \times 7$

3-7 GCF and LCM

1) What is the GCF of 36 and 180?

A) 12   B) 36   C) 4   D) 9

2) Solve.

Ramon has a box with 144 crackers. Kim has a box with 176 crackers. They want to divide each of their crackers equally to put into snack bags. The bags must all have the same number of crackers and as many crackers as possible. How many crackers should they put in each bag?

A) 18   B) 12   C) 14   D) 16

3) What is the GCF of 66 and 132?

A) 6   B) 11   C) 33   D) 66

4) What is the LCM of of 24 and 30?

A) 72   B) 240   C) 600   D) 120

5) What is the LCM of 15 and 40?

A) 120   B) 150   C) 240   D) 80

6) What is the least number of sports cards Jenna can have if she first puts them in groups of 25 with none left over and then puts them in groups of 35 with none left over?

A) 155   B) 175   C) 255   D) 285

3–8 Equivalent Fractions and Lowest Terms

1) Compare these fractions using < or >.

$\frac{14}{17}$ ☐ $\frac{16}{23}$

2) Which of these fractions is not equivalent to the others?

A) $\frac{18}{48}$ B) $\frac{16}{28}$ C) $\frac{12}{32}$ D) $\frac{9}{24}$

3) Which of these fractions is not equivalent to the others?

A) $\dfrac{18}{27}$ B) $\dfrac{6}{9}$ C) $\dfrac{16}{24}$ D) $\dfrac{30}{36}$

4) Express $\dfrac{30}{45}$ in lowest terms.

A) $\dfrac{2}{3}$ B) $\dfrac{8}{12}$ C) $\dfrac{6}{9}$ D) $\dfrac{8}{9}$

5) Which of these fractions is in lowest terms?

A) $\dfrac{12}{21}$ B) $\dfrac{7}{10}$ C) $\dfrac{6}{9}$ D) $\dfrac{12}{15}$

6) Express $\dfrac{20}{24}$ in lowest terms.

3-9 Comparing and Ordering Fractions

1) Which fraction is the greatest: $\dfrac{5}{9}$, $\dfrac{1}{2}$, $\dfrac{2}{3}$, $\dfrac{15}{24}$?

A) $\dfrac{1}{2}$ B) $\dfrac{2}{3}$ C) $\dfrac{5}{9}$ D) $\dfrac{15}{24}$

2) Which of these fractions is the least?

A) $\dfrac{3}{4}$ B) $\dfrac{11}{15}$ C) $\dfrac{7}{9}$ D) $\dfrac{3}{5}$

3) Which is greater, $\dfrac{19}{30}$ or $\dfrac{59}{60}$?

4) Which comparison is correct?

A) $47.02 < 470.2$ B) $0.7092 > 1.7092$
C) $8.21 < 8.07$ D) Not here

5) Which comparison is correct?

A) $0.2482 > 1.2482$ B) $62.56 < 6.256$
C) $8.54 < 8.07$ D) Not here

6) Solve.
Judy saved $73.44. Her brother saved $36.77. How much more money did Judy save?

A) $39.11   B) $36.33   C) $36.67   D) $36.11

7) Order these fractions from least to greatest.
$$\frac{9}{10}, \ \frac{6}{7}, \ \frac{8}{11}$$

3–10 Converting Between Fractions and Decimals

1) What decimal is equivalent to $\frac{4}{9}$?

A) $0.\overline{45}$ B) $0.\overline{5}$ C) $0.\overline{4}$ D) $0.4\overline{75}$

2) What decimal is equivalent to $\frac{7}{11}$?

A) $0.\overline{603}$ B) $0.\overline{63}$

C) $0.\overline{36}$ D) Not here

3) Convert $\frac{11}{12}$ to a decimal.

4) Convert 0.057 to a fraction in lowest terms.

A) $\frac{57}{10}$ B) $\frac{57}{100}$ C) $\frac{57}{1}$ D) $\frac{57}{1000}$

5) Convert 0.625 to a fraction in lowest terms.

A) $\frac{10}{16}$ B) $\frac{5}{8}$ C) $\frac{625}{1000}$ D) $\frac{625}{100}$

6) Convert $\frac{12}{25}$ to a fraction in lowest terms.

Chapter 3 Number Sense: Decimals and Fractions

Section 3A Decimal Concepts

3-1   Place Value: Comparing and Ordering Decimals

1)   Answer: D

2)   Answer: <

3)   Answer: <

3-2   Estimating by Rounding

1)   Answer: C

2)   Answer: B

3)   Answer: 2; 2,4; 2.41

4)   Answer: B

5)   Answer: B

6)   Answer: C

7)   Answer: C

8)   Answer: B

9)   Answer: C

3-3   Problem Solving   Sums and Differences of Decimals

1)   Answer: A

2)   Answer: D

3)   Answer: 0.818

3-4   Problem Solving   Products and Quotients of Decimals

1)   Answer: B

2)   Answer: A

3)   Answer: C

4)   Answer: D

5)   Answer: C

6)   Answer: C

3–5   Powers of 10 and Scientific Notation

1)   Answer: C

2)   Answer: B

3)   Answer: 10,000,000

4)   Answer: B

5)   Answer: A

6)   Answer: B

Section 3B Fraction Concepts

3–6   Divisibility and Prime Factorization

1)   Answer: B

2)   Answer: D

3)   Answer: 3, 7, and 9

4)   Answer: C

5)   Answer: C

6)   Answer: D

3–7   GCF and LCM

1)   Answer: B

2)   Answer: D

3)   Answer: D

4)   Answer: D

5)   Answer: A

6)   Answer: B

3–8 Equivalent Fractions and Lowest Terms

1) Answer: >

2) Answer: B

3) Answer: D

4) Answer: A

5) Answer: B

6) Answer: $\dfrac{5}{6}$

3–9 Comparing and Ordering Fractions

1) Answer: B

2) Answer: D

3) Answer: $\dfrac{59}{60}$

4) Answer: A

5) Answer: D

6) Answer: C

7) Answer: $\dfrac{8}{11}$, $\dfrac{6}{7}$, $\dfrac{9}{10}$

3–10 Converting Between Fractions and Decimals

1) Answer: C

2) Answer: B

3) Answer: $0.91\overline{6}$

4) Answer: D

5) Answer: B

6) Answer: $\dfrac{12}{25}$

Chapter 4 Operations with Fractions

Section 4A Sums and Differences of Fractions

4-1   Estimating: Fractions and Mixed Numbers

1) Estimate.

$$3\frac{5}{6} \ + \ 1\frac{1}{5}$$

A) 2   B) 5   C) 3   D) 4

2) Estimate.

$$15 \ \times \ \frac{1}{4}$$

A) 5   B) 6   C) 3   D) 4

3) Estimate.

$$26\frac{1}{7} \ \div \ 5\frac{1}{6}$$

A) 6   B) 3   C) 5   D) 4

4) Estimate.

$$8\frac{1}{5} \ - \ 2\frac{7}{8}$$

A) 6   B) 7   C) 5   D) $6\frac{1}{2}$

5) Estimate.

$$\frac{1}{12} \ + \ \frac{5}{8}$$

A) 2   B) 0   C) 1   D) $\frac{1}{2}$

6) Estimate the difference.

$$\frac{4}{5} \ - \ \frac{7}{12}$$

7) Estimate the sum.

$$\frac{3}{8} \ + \ \frac{5}{9}$$

4-2 Adding and Subtracting Fractions

1) Find the sum in lowest terms.

$$\frac{1}{9} + \frac{4}{9}$$

A) $\frac{5}{9}$ B) $\frac{3}{5}$ C) $\frac{7}{9}$ D) $\frac{4}{5}$

2) Find the difference in lowest terms.

$$\frac{18}{20} - \frac{6}{20}$$

A) $\frac{12}{20}$ B) $\frac{1}{5}$ C) $\frac{4}{20}$ D) $\frac{3}{5}$

3) Find the sum in lowest terms.

$$\frac{5}{8} + \frac{1}{4}$$

A) $\frac{7}{8}$ B) $\frac{6}{12}$ C) $\frac{3}{4}$ D) $\frac{6}{8}$

4) Find the difference in lowest terms.

$$\frac{18}{21} - \frac{4}{14}$$

A) 0 B) $\frac{4}{7}$ C) $\frac{12}{7}$ D) $\frac{2}{7}$

5) Find the sum in lowest terms.

$$\frac{2}{3} + \frac{1}{5}$$

6) Find the difference in lowest terms.

$$\frac{17}{18} - \frac{5}{18}$$

7) Find the difference in lowest terms.

$$\frac{5}{6} - \frac{3}{18}$$

A) $\frac{2}{3}$ B) $\frac{2}{12}$ C) $\frac{13}{18}$ D) $\frac{2}{6}$

8) Solve. $n + \frac{5}{8} = \frac{3}{4}$

A) $n = \frac{1}{8}$ B) $n = \frac{3}{4}$

C) $n = \frac{5}{8}$ D) $n = \frac{3}{8}$

9) Solve.

$$m - \frac{3}{5} = \frac{3}{10}$$

A) $m = \frac{9}{10}$ B) $m = \frac{3}{10}$

C) $m = \frac{3}{5}$ D) $m = \frac{6}{10}$

10) Solve. $\frac{1}{8} + p = \frac{5}{16}$

A) $p = \frac{1}{16}$ B) $p = \frac{3}{16}$

C) $p = \frac{5}{16}$ D) $p = \frac{7}{16}$

11) Solve. $r - \dfrac{1}{4} = \dfrac{7}{12}$

A) $r = \dfrac{3}{4}$ B) $r = \dfrac{1}{2}$

C) $r = \dfrac{5}{6}$ D) $r = \dfrac{2}{3}$

12) Solve. $a - \dfrac{2}{3} = \dfrac{3}{9}$

13) Solve. $\dfrac{3}{5} + b = \dfrac{2}{3}$

A) $\dfrac{5}{15}$ B) $\dfrac{1}{2}$ C) $\dfrac{5}{8}$ D) $\dfrac{1}{15}$

14) Solve. $c - \dfrac{1}{5} = \dfrac{3}{7}$

4–3   Adding and Subtracting Mixed Numbers

1) Find the difference in lowest terms.
$4\dfrac{3}{8} - 2\dfrac{1}{8}$

A) $2\dfrac{1}{4}$ B) $1\dfrac{1}{4}$ C) $1\dfrac{1}{2}$ D) $2\dfrac{1}{2}$

2) Find the sum in lowest terms.
$4\dfrac{1}{7} + 3\dfrac{5}{7}$

A) $7\dfrac{3}{7}$ B) $7\dfrac{5}{7}$ C) $7\dfrac{6}{7}$ D) $7\dfrac{4}{7}$

3) Find the difference in lowest terms.

$9 - 6\frac{5}{9}$

A) $3\frac{4}{9}$ 　　　　B) $2\frac{4}{9}$ 　　　　C) $3\frac{5}{9}$ 　　　　D) $2\frac{5}{9}$

4) Find the sum in lowest terms.

$1\frac{1}{6} + 5\frac{1}{5}$

A) $6\frac{13}{40}$ 　　　B) $6\frac{2}{13}$ 　　　C) $6\frac{11}{30}$ 　　　D) $6\frac{2}{11}$

5) A can contained $6\frac{1}{8}$ oz. of juice. Then $4\frac{3}{8}$ oz. of the juice was used in a smoothie. How much juice was left in the can?

A) $1\frac{1}{2}$ oz. 　　B) $2\frac{1}{4}$ oz. 　　C) $1\frac{3}{4}$ oz. 　　D) $2\frac{1}{2}$ oz.

6) Marie is hiking on a trail that is $8\frac{1}{4}$ mi long. A trail marker says she is $4\frac{5}{8}$ mi from the start of the trail. How far does she have to hike to reach the end of the trail.

7) Two books are being sent in a package. One book weighs $\frac{5}{6}$ lb and the other weighs $1\frac{1}{6}$ lb. What is their combined weight?

8)   Solve. $x + 3\frac{3}{4} = 6\frac{1}{9}$

   A) $x = 2\frac{13}{36}$ B) $x = 2\frac{1}{18}$

   C) $x = 9\frac{13}{36}$ D) $x = 3\frac{13}{36}$

9)   Solve. $8\frac{1}{6} + y = 14\frac{2}{5}$

   A) $y = 6\frac{7}{30}$ B) $y = 22$

   C) $y = 6\frac{1}{6}$ D) $y = 6\frac{1}{5}$

10)   Solve. $k - 4\frac{1}{3} = 5\frac{3}{7}$

11)   Solve. $w - 6\frac{1}{3} = 9\frac{3}{8}$

   A) $w = 3\frac{2}{5}$ B) $w = 15\frac{17}{24}$

   C) $w = 3\frac{17}{24}$ D)   Not here

12)   Solve. $c + 5\frac{4}{9} = 9\frac{3}{5}$

13)   Solve. $a - 4\frac{3}{4} = 2\frac{1}{3}$

14)   Solve. $14\frac{1}{4} + y = 17\frac{3}{8}$

Section 4B Products and Quotients of Fractions

4-4 Multiplying Fractions

1) Find the product in lowest terms.

$$\frac{2}{5} \times \frac{5}{9}$$

2) Find the product in lowest terms.

$$\frac{8}{9} \times \frac{5}{16}$$

A) $\dfrac{10}{18}$

B) $\dfrac{40}{18}$

C) $\dfrac{20}{9}$

D) Not here

3) Find the product in lowest terms.

$$\frac{8}{15} \times \frac{5}{16}$$

A) $\dfrac{1}{8}$

B) $\dfrac{1}{6}$

C) $\dfrac{1}{5}$

D) $\dfrac{1}{10}$

4) Find the product in lowest terms.

$$\frac{16}{45} \times \frac{15}{24}$$

A) $\dfrac{4}{27}$

B) $\dfrac{2}{9}$

C) $\dfrac{4}{9}$

D) $\dfrac{2}{18}$

5) Find the product in lowest terms.

$$\frac{6}{15} \times \frac{4}{12}$$

6) Find the product in lowest terms.

$$\frac{5}{7} \times \frac{7}{9}$$

7) Brian wants to ride his bike 650 miles this summer. He has already ridden $\frac{3}{5}$ of his goal. How many miles has he ridden so far?

4–5   Multiplying Mixed Numbers

1) Find the product in lowest terms.
$6\frac{4}{9} \times 5\frac{12}{15}$

A) $30\frac{2}{3}$ B) $30\frac{8}{15}$ C) $39\frac{9}{15}$ D) $37\frac{17}{45}$

2) Find the product in lowest terms.
$2\frac{2}{7} \times 4\frac{1}{3}$

3) Find the product in lowest terms.
$3\frac{1}{6} \times 8\frac{3}{5}$

A) $24\frac{1}{10}$ B) $27\frac{7}{30}$

C) $28\frac{7}{30}$ D) Not here

4) Find the product in lowest terms.
$1\frac{1}{8} \times 6\frac{2}{3}$

5) Find the product in lowest terms.
$4\frac{1}{5} \times 2\frac{1}{3}$

6) Juan has collected 380 stamps. If Renzo has collected $3\frac{1}{4}$ times as many stamps as Juan has, how many stamps does Renzo have?

A) 1,200 stamps
B) 1,330 stamps
C) 1,235 stamps
D) 1,140 stamps

7) Rulers that weigh $4\frac{1}{3}$ oz each are packed 12 to a box. How much do all the rulers in a box weigh?

4-6 Dividing Fractions and Mixed Numbers

1) Find the quotient in lowest terms.

$\frac{5}{6} \div \frac{3}{7}$

2) Find the quotient in lowest terms.

$\frac{1}{5} \div \frac{7}{10}$

A) $\frac{5}{7}$
B) $\frac{7}{50}$
C) $\frac{2}{7}$
D) $\frac{1}{10}$

3) Find the quotient in lowest terms.

$\frac{2}{9} \div \frac{1}{3}$

A) $\frac{1}{6}$
B) $\frac{2}{3}$
C) $\frac{6}{9}$
D) $\frac{2}{27}$

4) Find the quotient in lowest terms.

$5 \div \frac{10}{12}$

5) Find the quotient in lowest terms.

$1\frac{3}{7} \div 1\frac{2}{3}$

6) Caroline has a $20\frac{1}{4}$-ft piece of ribbon that she wants to cut into 6 pieces that are all the same size. how long should each piece of ribbon be?

7) Clay bricks that are $6\frac{3}{4}$ in. long are being used in a garden border that is $33\frac{3}{4}$ in. long. How many bricks are needed?

Chapter 4 Operations with Fractions

Section 4A Sums and Differences of Fractions

4-1   Estimating: Fractions and Mixed Numbers

1)   Answer: B

2)   Answer: D

3)   Answer: C

4)   Answer: C

5)   Answer: D

6)   Answer: $\dfrac{1}{2}$

7)   Answer: 1

4-2   Adding and Subtracting Fractions

1)   Answer: A

2)   Answer: D

3)   Answer: A

4)   Answer: B

5)   Answer: $\dfrac{13}{15}$

6)   Answer: $\dfrac{2}{3}$

7)   Answer: A

8)   Answer: A

9)   Answer: A

10)   Answer: B

11)   Answer: C

12) Answer: $a = 1$

13) Answer: D

14) Answer: $c = \dfrac{22}{35}$

4-3 Adding and Subtracting Mixed Numbers

1) Answer: A

2) Answer: C

3) Answer: B

4) Answer: C

5) Answer: C

6) Answer: $3\dfrac{5}{8}$ mi

7) Answer: 2 lb

8) Answer: A

9) Answer: A

10) Answer: $k = 9\dfrac{16}{21}$

11) Answer: B

12) Answer: $c = 4\dfrac{7}{45}$

13) Answer: $a = 7\dfrac{1}{12}$

14) Answer: $y = 3\dfrac{1}{8}$

Section 4B Products and Quotients of Fractions

4-4 Multiplying Fractions

1) Answer: $\dfrac{2}{9}$

2) Answer: D

3) Answer: B

4) Answer: B

5) Answer: $\dfrac{2}{15}$

6) Answer: $\dfrac{5}{9}$

7) Answer: 390 miles

4-5 Multiplying Mixed Numbers

1) Answer: D

2) Answer: $9\dfrac{19}{21}$

3) Answer: B

4) Answer: $7\dfrac{1}{2}$

5) Answer: $9\dfrac{4}{5}$

6) Answer: C

7) Answer: 52 oz

4-6 Dividing Fractions and Mixed Numbers

1) Answer: $1\dfrac{17}{18}$

2) Answer: C

3)   Answer: B

4)   Answer: 6

5)   Answer: $\frac{6}{7}$

6)   Answer: $3\frac{3}{8}$ ft

7)   Answer: 5   bricks

Chapter 5 Geometry and Measurement

Section 5A Geometric Figures

5-1 Angles

1) What word describes an angle with a measure of 14°?
   A) Complementary   B) Obtuse
   C) Right   D) Acute

2) Classify an angle that measures 23°.

3) What is the supplement of an angle that measures 178°?
   A) 72°   B) 92°   C) 102°   D) 12°

4) What angle is supplementary to an angle of 77°?
   A) 73°   B) 103°   C) 13°   D) 93°

5) What angle is complementary to an angle of 69°?
   A) 26°   B) 16°   C) 21°   D) 11°

6) Classify an angle that measures 136°.
   A) Right   B) Complementary
   C) Obtuse   D) Acute

5-2 Parallel and Perpendicular Lines

1)

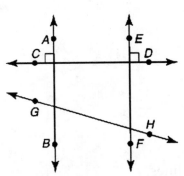

Name a pair of parallel lines.
   A) $\overleftrightarrow{AB}$ and $\overleftrightarrow{EF}$ B) $\overleftrightarrow{CD}$ and $\overleftrightarrow{EF}$
   C) $\overleftrightarrow{CD}$ and $\overleftrightarrow{GH}$ D) $\overleftrightarrow{AB}$ and $\overleftrightarrow{CD}$

2) The opposite sides of a rhombus are _____.
   A) Perpendicular   B) Skewed
   C) Parallel   D) Acute

3)

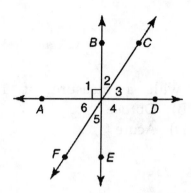

Name a pair of complementary angles.

A) ∠1, ∠2   B) ∠1, ∠6   C) ∠2, ∠3   D) ∠4, ∠5

4)

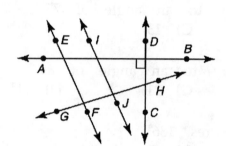

What line is perpendicular to $\overleftrightarrow{CD}$?

A) $\overleftrightarrow{AB}$ B) $\overleftrightarrow{EF}$ C) $\overleftrightarrow{GH}$ D) $\overleftrightarrow{IJ}$

5)

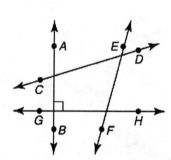

Name a pair of perpendicular lines.

6)   A pair of lines that intersect in a right angle are _____.

5-3 Triangles and Quadrilaterals

1) Classify a triangle in which two angles are congruent.
    A) Equilateral
    B) Right
    C) Isosceles
    D) Scalene

2) Classify a triangle that has angles that measure 80°, 60°, and 40°.
    A) Right
    B) Acute
    C) Equilateral
    D) Obtuse

3) Which of these is always true of obtuse triangles?
    A) There is one angle greater than 90°.
    B) Two angles have the same measure.
    C) There is one right angle.
    D) All three sides are different lengths.

4)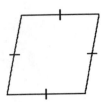

    Classify the quadrilateral as many ways as you can.

5) What quadrilateral can have only one pair of parallel sides and one pair of congruent sides?
    A) Rhombus   B) Trapezoid   C) Rectangle   D) Square

6) What closed 4-sided figure has four right angles and exactly two pairs of congruent sides?
    A) Square
    B) Rectangle
    C) Parallelogram
    D) Rhombus

7) In triangle DEF, if m∠D = 60° and m∠E = 70°, what is the measure of ∠F?

8) If m∠E = 100° and m∠F = 50° in triangle DEF, what is the measure of ∠D?
    A) 40°   B) 150°   C) 30°   D) 20°

9)   If ∠A = 91° and m∠B = 30° in triangle ABC, what is the measure of ∠C?

5-4   Polygons

1)

Is this a regular polygon?

2)   Which of these is true?
A) No hexagons are regular polygons.
B) Some hexagons are not regular polygons.
C) All hexagons are regular polygons.
D) All regular polygons are hexagons.

3)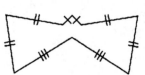

Is this figure a regular polygon?

4)   What is the sum of the angle measures of an octagon?
A) 360°   B) 540°   C) 720°   D) 1,080°

5)   What is the sum of the angle measues of a 6-sided polygon?
A) 720°   B) 360°   C) 1,080°   D) 540°

6)   Find the sum of the angle measures of a decagon.

5-5   Perimeter and Area

1)   What is the area of a rectangle with length 25 m and width 17 m?

A) 92 m^2 B) 84 m^2 C) 425 m^2 D) 42 m^2

2)   What is the perimeter of a rectangle with length 28 ft and width 10 ft?

A) 280 ft   B) 48 ft   C) 76 ft   D) 66 ft

3)   Find the perimeter and area of a rectanglular garden that measures 73 m × 22 m.

Section 5B Geometric Formulas

5-6   Squares and Square Roots

1)   Find the square of 49.
A) 2,401   B) 980   C) 343   D) 7

2)   Find the square of 22.
A) 2,222   B) 66   C) 484   D) 44

3)   Find the square of 49.

4)   Find the square root of 225.
A) 50,625   B) 30   C) 450   D) 15

5)   Find the square root of 15 rounded to two decimal places.
A) 3.9   B) 3.87   C) 3.8   D) 3.88

6)   Use a calculator to find the square root of 232. Round the answer to two decimal places.

5-7   The Pythagorean Theorem

1)   Find the missing side length.

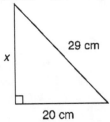

A) 25 cm   B) 24 cm   C) 20 cm   D) 21 cm

2) Find the missing length in the right triangle.

3) Find the missing side length in a right triangle with a leg of 80 ft and a hypotenuse of 170 ft.

4) Find the hypotenuse of a right triangle with one leg of 10 in. and the other leg 24 in.

5) Which are the lengths of sides in a right triangle?
   A) 22, 27, 28   B) 5, 7, 10
   C) 8, 14, 15   D) 14, 48, 50

6) What is the length of the hypotenuse of a right triangle with legs 16 m and 30 m?

   A) 52 m   B) 55 m   C) 34 m   D) 58 m

5–8 Areas of Triangles

1) What is the area of a triangle with b = 22 ft and h = 20 ft?
   A) 220 ft^2 B) 440 ft^2 C) 880 ft^2 D) 110 ft^2

2) What is the area of a triangle with a base of 33 cm and a height of 12 cm?

3) What is the area of the triangle?

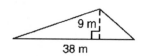

5-9   Areas of Parallelograms and Trapezoids

1) What is the area of a parallelogram with b = 38 in. and
   h = 5 in.

   A) 380 in^2 B) 190 in^2 C) 95 in^2 D) 114 in^2

2) What is the area of the parallelogram?

   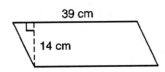

3) Find the area of a rectangle with a base of 11 ft and height of 5.2 ft.

4) What is the area of a trapezoid with b_1 = 12 m, b_2 = 21 m, and h = 90 m?

5) What is the area of the trapezoid?

   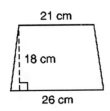

   A) 846 cm^2 B) 423 cm^2
   C) 4,914 cm^2 D) 9,828 cm^2

6) Find the area of a trapezoid with bases of 32 ft and 46 ft and height of 9 ft.

5-10 Problem Solving   Areas of Irregular Figures

1)

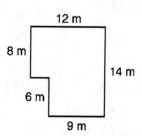

What is the area of the figure?
A) $150 \ m^2$ B) $168 \ m^2$ C) $432 \ m^2$ D) $84 \ m^2$

2)   Find the area of the figure.

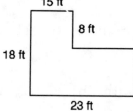

3)   Find the area of the figure.

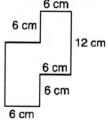

Chapter 5 Geometry and Measurement

Section 5A Geometric Figures

5-1 Angles

1) Answer: D

2) Answer: Acute

3) Answer: C

4) Answer: B

5) Answer: C

6) Answer: C

5-2 Parallel and Perpendicular Lines

1) Answer: A

2) Answer: C

3) Answer: C

4) Answer: A

5) Answer: $\overleftrightarrow{AB}$, $\overleftrightarrow{GH}$

6) Answer: Perpendicular

5-3 Triangles and Quadrilaterals

1) Answer: C

2) Answer: B

3) Answer: A

4) Answer: rhombus, parallelogram

5) Answer: B

6) Answer: B

7) Answer: 50°

8) Answer: C

9) Answer: 59°

5–4   Polygons

1) Answer: No

2) Answer: B

3) Answer: No

4) Answer: D

5) Answer: A

6) Answer: 1,440°

5–5   Perimeter and Area

1) Answer: C

2) Answer: C

3) Answer: 190 m; 1,606 m^2

Section 5B Geometric Formulas

5–6   Squares and Square Roots

1) Answer: A

2) Answer: C

3) Answer: 2,401

4) Answer: D

5) Answer: B

6) Answer: 15.23

5–7   The Pythagorean Theorem

1) Answer: D

2) Answer: 34

3) Answer: 150 ft

4) Answer: 26 in.

5)   Answer: D

6)   Answer: C

5-8   Areas of Triangles

1)   Answer: A

2)   Answer: 198 cm^2

3)   Answer: 171 m^2

5-9   Areas of Parallelograms and Trapezoids

1)   Answer: B

2)   Answer: 546 cm^2

3)   Answer: 57.2 ft^2

4)   Answer: 1,485 m^2

5)   Answer: B

6)   Answer: 351 ft^2

5-10 Problem Solving   Areas of Irregular Figures

1)   Answer: A

2)   Answer: 350 ft^2

3)   Answer: 144 cm^2

Chapter 6 Ratios, Rates, and Proportions

Section 6A Ratios and Rates

6-1   Exploring and Estimating Ratios

1) Which of these is *not* a ratio equivalent to the ratio of 7 children to 11 adults?

A) 7 to 11

B) 11:7

C) 14 to 22

D) $\dfrac{7}{11}$

2) What is a ratio equivalent to 3 oranges to 8 pears?

A) $\dfrac{3}{8}$　　B) 8 to 3　　C) 3 to 16　　D) 8:3

3) What is a ratio equivalent to the ratio of 28 shirts to 12 shorts?

A) 28 to 12

B) 12:28

C) $\dfrac{12}{28}$

D) 6:14

4) Write the ratio in three ways. Write in lowest terms.

15 lions to 35 tigers

5) Write the ratio in three ways. Write in lowest terms.

94 points in 4 quarters

6) What is the ratio of 8 teams to 64 players written in lowest terms?

A) 1:8　　　B) 8:8　　　C) $\dfrac{8}{1}$　　　D) 8 to 64

7) What is the ratio of 16 apples to 4 oranges written in lowest terms?

A) $\dfrac{16}{4}$　　　B) 4 to 16　　C) $\dfrac{4}{1}$　　　D) 2:4

8) What is the ratio of 106 points in 4 games written in lowest terms?

A) 106:4

B) 53 to 2

C) $\frac{2}{53}$

D) Not here

9) Write a ratio to compare the quantities.

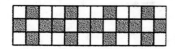

The shaded squares to all the squares

A) $\frac{36}{12}$

B) $\frac{9}{4}$

C) $\frac{4}{9}$

D) $\frac{9}{36}$

10) Write a ratio to compare the quantities.

A —— 8 cm —— M — 4 cm — C

The length of $\overline{AM}$ to the length of $\overline{AC}$

A) $\frac{1}{2}$

B) $\frac{2}{3}$

C) $\frac{3}{4}$

D) $\frac{3}{2}$

6-2 Exploring and Estimating Rates

1) Which of these is the best buy for napkins all the same size and brand?

A) 12 for $1.00

B) 5 for $0.49

C) 70 for $6.00

D) 25 for $3.50

2) Use unit prices to determine which is the better buy.
$5.95 for 7 pounds or $4.50 for 5 pounds

3) Use unit prices to determine which is the better buy.
3 oranges for 65 cents or 5 for a dollar

4) Use unit prices to determine which is the better buy.
6 jars for $3.40 or 4 jars for $2.40

5) Use unit prices to determine which is the best buy.

$1.60 for 3 pounds, $2.30 for 4 pounds, $1.25 for 2 pounds, or $2.80 for 5 pounds

6) Express as a unit rate: 8 degrees in 4 hours

7) Express as a unit rate: 250 miles in 4 hours

8) Express as a unit rate:
392 points in 4 games of basketball

9) Express 96 people to 8 buses as a unit rate.

10) Express 304 players to 19 coaches as a unit rate.

6-3   Equivalent Ratios and Rates

1) What ratio is equivalent to $\frac{3}{7}$?

A) $\frac{6}{21}$ B) $\frac{6}{14}$ C) $\frac{9}{14}$ D) $\frac{6}{28}$

2) What rate is equivalent to $\frac{285 \text{ miles}}{8 \text{ hours}}$?

A) $\frac{570 \text{ miles}}{16 \text{ hours}}$ B) $\frac{57 \text{ miles}}{2 \text{ hours}}$

C) $\frac{34.5 \text{ miles}}{1 \text{ hour}}$ D) $\frac{57 \text{ miles}}{4 \text{ hours}}$

3) Multiply and divide to find two ratios equivalent to $\frac{16}{22}$.

4) Multiply and divide to find two ratios equivalent to each given ratio.

a. $\dfrac{12}{45}$

b. $\dfrac{50}{150}$

6–4 Using Tables to Explore Ratios and Rates

1) Which table is an equivalent ratio table?

A)
2	12	18	40
3	18	27	60

B)
4	20	40	100
5	30	60	150

C)
2	20	40	200
3	40	50	500

D)
4	6	8	10
5	7	9	11

2) Use multiplication to complete the table by finding five ratios equivalent to $\dfrac{5}{8}$.

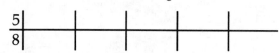

A)
5	10	15	20	25	30
8	16	18	24	32	36

B)
5	10	15	20	25	30
8	16	24	32	40	48

C)
5	10	15	20	25	30
8	13	18	23	28	33

D)
5	10	15	20	25	30
8	10	11	12	13	14

3) Using multiplication, complete the table by finding five ratios equivalent to $\frac{3}{11}$.

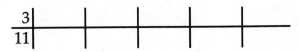

A) | 3 | 6 | 9 | 12 | 15 | 18 |
   |---|---|---|----|----|----|
   | 11 | 22 | 33 | 44 | 55 | 66 |

B) | 3 | 4 | 6 | 8 | 10 | 12 |
   |---|---|---|---|----|----|
   | 11 | 12 | 14 | 16 | 18 | 20 |

C) | 3 | 9 | 6 | 9 | 12 | 12 |
   |---|---|---|---|----|----|
   | 11 | 22 | 33 | 44 | 33 | 44 |

D) | 3 | 6 | 9 | 12 | 15 | 18 |
   |---|---|---|----|----|----|
   | 11 | 33 | 33 | 44 | 44 | 55 |

4) Using multiplication, complete the table by finding five ratios equivalent to $\frac{12}{11}$.

5) Which table is an equivalent–ratio table?

A) | 7 | 8 | 9 | 10 | 11 | 12 |
   |---|---|---|----|----|----|
   | 3 | 4 | 5 | 6 | 7 | 8 |

B) | 7 | 14 | 21 | 28 | 35 | 42 |
   |---|----|----|----|----|----|
   | 3 | 6 | 9 | 12 | 15 | 21 |

C) | 7 | 14 | 21 | 28 | 35 | 42 |
   |---|----|----|----|----|----|
   | 3 | 6 | 9 | 12 | 15 | 18 |

D) | 7 | 14 | 21 | 28 | 35 | 42 |
   |---|----|----|----|----|----|
   | 3 | 5 | 6 | 7 | 8 | 9 |

Section 6B Proportional Quantities

6-5 Creating Proportions

1) Which proportion is *not* made up of ratios equivalent to $\frac{15}{8}$?

A) $\frac{45}{24} = \frac{60}{32}$

B) $\frac{60}{32} = \frac{30}{16}$

C) $\frac{30}{16} = \frac{75}{40}$

D) $\frac{45}{32} = \frac{75}{40}$

2) Which proportion is *not* made up of ratios equivalent to $\frac{5}{7}$?

A) $\frac{35}{42} = \frac{50}{56}$

B) $\frac{40}{56} = \frac{25}{35}$

C) $\frac{15}{21} = \frac{30}{42}$

D) $\frac{35}{49} = \frac{150}{210}$

3) Complete the equivalent ratio table. Then write four proportions involving the ratios in the table.

4	8	12	16
9			

4) Complete the equivalent ratio table. Then write four proportions involving the ratios in the table.

3	6	9	12
11			

6-6 Testing for Proportionality

1) Which of these are proportional?

i) $\frac{4}{9} \stackrel{?}{=} \frac{32}{40}$

ii) $\frac{24}{54} \stackrel{?}{=} \frac{72}{162}$

A) Both i and ii

B) i

C) ii

D) Neither i nor ii

2) Which of these are proportional?

i) $\frac{5}{14} \stackrel{?}{=} \frac{20}{56}$

ii) $\frac{0.75}{1} \stackrel{?}{=} \frac{3}{4}$

A) Both i and ii

B) ii

C) i

D) Neither i nor ii

3) Which of these are proportional?

   i) $\dfrac{14}{18} \overset{?}{=} \dfrac{126}{162}$ ii) $\dfrac{7}{9} \overset{?}{=} \dfrac{84}{108}$

4) Decide if the ratios are proportional:

   $\dfrac{5}{16} \overset{?}{=} \dfrac{25}{80}$

5) Which of these is an equation that has equal cross-products?
   A) Terms   B) Proportion
   C) Ratio   D) Not here

6-7 Solving Proportions Using Unit Rates

1) Camille saved $184 in 8 months. At that rate, how long will it take her to save the $345 she needs to buy her favorite print?

   A) 15 months   B) 18 months
   C) 21 months   D) 12 months

2) Carlos drove 428 miles in 8 hours. At that rate, how long will it take him to drive 642 miles?

   A) 9 hours   B) 14 hours   C) 12 hours   D) 10 hours

3) Jeff earned $38.50 in 7 hours.
   a. Find Jeff's hourly rate.

   b. At this rate, how much will he earn in 20 hours?

4) Rita drove 286 miles in 5 hours.
   a. Find Rita's rate per hour.

   b. At this rate, how many miles will she drive in 3 hours?

6–8   Cross Multiplication

1) Solve the proportion:

$$\frac{3}{9} = \frac{69}{x}$$

2) Solve this proportion:

$$\frac{5}{16} = \frac{x}{128}$$

A) $x = 50$ B) $x = 20$
C) $x = 40$ D) $x = 8$

3) Solve this proportion:

$$\frac{19}{35} = \frac{x}{17.5}$$

A) $x = 12.5$ B) $x = 8$
C) $x = 38$ D) $x = 9.5$

4) Solve this proportion:

$$\frac{9}{26} = \frac{54}{x}$$

A) $x = 256$ B) $x = 156$
C) $x = 324$ D) $x = 234$

5) Which of the following is a proportion?

A) $\frac{3}{8} \overset{?}{=} \frac{15}{48}$ B) $\frac{42}{64} \overset{?}{=} \frac{14}{16}$

C) $\frac{90}{102} \overset{?}{=} \frac{15}{17}$ D) $\frac{49}{64} \overset{?}{=} \frac{7}{8}$

6) Is the following a proportion?

$$\frac{3}{5} \stackrel{?}{=} \frac{24}{40}$$

7) For the following, find the cross products and state whether or not it is a proportion.

$$\frac{5}{6} \stackrel{?}{=} \frac{75}{90}$$

Chapter 6 Ratios, Rates, and Proportions

Section 6A Ratios and Rates

6-1 Exploring and Estimating Ratios

1) Answer: B

2) Answer: A

3) Answer: A

4) Answer: $\frac{3}{7}$, 3:7, 3 to 7

5) Answer: $\frac{47}{2}$, 47:2, 47 to 2

6) Answer: A

7) Answer: C

8) Answer: B

9) Answer: C

10) Answer: B

6-2 Exploring and Estimating Rates

1) Answer: A

2) Answer: $5.95 for 7 pounds

3) Answer: 5 for $1.00

4) Answer: 6 jars for $3.40

5) Answer: $1.60 for 3 pounds

6) Answer: $\frac{2 \text{ degrees}}{1 \text{ hour}}$

7) Answer: $\frac{62.5 \text{ mi}}{1 \text{ hour}}$

8) Answer: $\dfrac{98 \;\; \text{points}}{1 \;\; \text{game}}$

9) Answer: $\dfrac{12 \;\; \text{people}}{1 \;\; \text{bus}}$

10) Answer: $\dfrac{16 \;\; \text{players}}{1 \;\; \text{coach}}$

6-3   Equivalent Ratios and Rates

1) Answer: B

2) Answer: A

3) Answer: Possible answers: $\dfrac{32}{44}$ and $\dfrac{8}{11}$

4) Answer:
   a. Possible answers: $\dfrac{24}{90}$ and $\dfrac{4}{15}$

   b. Possible answers: $\dfrac{100}{300}$ and $\dfrac{1}{3}$

6-4   Using Tables to Explore Ratios and Rates

1) Answer: A

2) Answer: B

3) Answer: A

4) Answer:

12	24	36	48	60	72
11	22	33	44	55	66

5) Answer: C

Section 6B Proportional Quantities

6-5   Creating Proportions

1) Answer: D

2) Answer: A

3) Answer:

$$\begin{array}{c|c|c|c}4 & 8 & 12 & 16 \\ \hline 9 & 18 & 27 & 36\end{array}$$

Possible proportions:

$$\frac{4}{9} = \frac{8}{18}; \quad \frac{4}{9} = \frac{12}{27}$$

$$\frac{4}{9} = \frac{16}{36}; \quad \frac{8}{18} = \frac{16}{36}$$

4) Answer:

$$\begin{array}{c|c|c|c}3 & 6 & 9 & 12 \\ \hline 11 & 22 & 33 & 44\end{array}$$

Possible proportions:

$$\frac{3}{11} = \frac{6}{22}; \quad \frac{3}{11} = \frac{9}{33}$$

$$\frac{3}{11} = \frac{12}{44}; \quad \frac{6}{22} = \frac{12}{44}$$

6-6   Testing for Proportionality

1) Answer: C

2) Answer: A

3) Answer: Both i and ii

4) Answer: Yes

5) Answer: B

6-7   Solving Proportions Using Unit Rates

1) Answer: A

2) Answer: C

3) Answer: a. $5.5/hr   b. $110

4) Answer: a. 57.2 mi/hr
            b. 171.6 miles

6-8   Cross Multiplication

1) Answer: $x = 207$

2) Answer: C

3)   Answer: D

4)   Answer: B

5)   Answer: C

6)   Answer: yes

7)   Answer: 360,   360;   yes

Chapter 7 Proportion, Scale, and Similarity

Section 7A Scale Drawings, Maps, and Scales

7-1 Measurement: Estimating Actual and Scale Distances

1) Find the scale of a map if a 12 mile trail is shown as 3 inches long.

   A) 1 in. to 2 mi B) 1 in. to 4 mi
   C) 1 in. to 6 mi D) 1 in. to 3 mi

2) Find the scale of a map if a 30 kilometer road is shown as 5 centimeters long.

   A) 1 cm = 7 km B) 1 cm = 8 km
   C) 1 cm = 9 km D) 1 cm = 6 km

3) Two lakes are 24 miles apart. How far apart do they appear on a map with a scale of 1 inch = 16 miles?

4) Two towns are 32 cm apart on a map with the scale 9 cm: 90 km. What is the actual distance between them?

   A) 320 cm   B) 810 cm   C) 320 km   D) 810 km

5) Two cities are 64 inches apart on a map with the scale 4 in.: 40 mi. What is the actual distance between them?

   A) 640 mi   B) 2560 mi   C) 16 mi   D) 10 mi

6) Reed plans to drive from his house to the lake. On a map with the scale 1 in. = 20 mi, the lake is 2 inches from his house. If Reed leaves at 8:30 A.M. and drives at 40 mi/hr, when will he arrive at the lake?

   A) 10:00 A.M. B) 9:00 A.M.
   C) 9:30 A.M. D) 10:30 A.M.

7-2 Calculating with Scales

1) A drawing of a museum uses the scale 1 in. = 4 ft. In the drawing, the museum is 2 feet tall. How tall is the actual museum?

A) 96 in.   B) 8 ft   C) 8 in.   D) 96 ft

2) Solve.
A model of a boat uses the scale 1 in. = 4 ft. The model has a deck length of 17.5 in. How long is the actual deck?

A) 12 ft   B) 70 ft   C) 52.5 ft   D) 52.5 in.

3) On a scale drawing, 4 inches represents an actual length of 160 feet.

a. What length on the scale drawing represents 40 feet?

b. What actual length does 0.5 inch on the scale drawing represent?

7-3 Problem Solving   Using Maps

1) Ty left for Southvale at 10:00 A.M. and traveled 486 miles without crossing any time zones. She arrived at 7:00 P.M. that evening. What was the average speed of the bus?

A) 56 mi/hr   B) 52 mi/hr
C) 54 mi/hr   D) 58 mi/hr

2) Solve.
Jamal left for Seaside at 6 a.m. he traveled at 52 mi/hr and arrived at 10 a.m. How far did Jamal travel?

A) 312 mi   B) 4 mi   C) 208 mi   D) 7 mi

3) Cuong plans to drive his car to a hiking trail 140 miles away. He wants to arrive at 9 A.M. to meet his friends. If he drives at an average speed of 56 mi/hr, when should he leave?

A) 6:30 A.M.   B) 8:00 A.M.
C) 7:30 A.M.   D) 6:00 A.M.

7–4   Creating Scale Drawings and Scale Models

1) Solve.
A building is 40 m tall and 20 m wide. What is approximately the largest scale that could be used to make a drawing of the building fit on an 8.5 in. × 11 in. sheet of paper?

A) 1 in. = 5 m   B) 1 in. = 3 m
C) 1 in. = 4 m   D) 1 in. = 6 m

2) What approximate scale should be used to make the largest possible scale drawing of a 30 ft × 30 ft object on an
8.5 in. × 11 in. sheet of paper?

A) 1 in. = 4 ft   B) 1 in. = 3 ft
C) 1 in. = 5 ft   D) 1 in. = 6 ft

3) What approximate scale would you use to make the largest possible model of a 48 foot statue so that it fits into a display case that is $6\frac{1}{2}$ inches tall?

A) 1 in. = 3 ft   B) 1 in. = 2 ft
C) 0.5 in. = 6 ft   D) 0.5 in. = 4 ft

Section 7B Dimensional Analysis

7–5   Choosing Appropriate Rates and Units

1) What are appropriate units to describe the speed of a train?

2) What are appropriate units to describe the rate at which fruit is sold in a grocery store?

3) What are appropriate units to describe the speed of a snail?

4) What reciprocal unit rate has the same meaning as 2 min/1 km?

A) 0.04 km/1 min   B) 0.02 km/1 min
C) 0.5 km/1 min   D) 0.2 km/1 min

5) What reciprocal unit rate has the same meaning as $\frac{1}{11}$ min/1 mi?

A) $\frac{1}{11}$ mi/1 min   B) 110 mi/1 min

C) 11 mi/1 min   D) $\frac{1}{11}$ mi/11 min

6) Solve.
The sandwich shop sells 87 sandwiches each week day. How many does it sell in a five day work week (Monday through Friday)?

7-6 Converting Units

1) Convert 450 inches to yards.
A) 37.5 feet   B) 37.5 yards
C) 12.5 yards   D) 150 feet

2) Convert 26 quarts to gallons.
A) 6.5 gallons   B) 52 gallons
C) 13 gallons   D) 3.25 gallons

3) Convert $30 per yard to dollars per foot.

7-7   Problem Solving   Converting Rates

1) What rate is equivalent to 1800 mi/hr?

   A) 30 mi/day   B) 0.5 mi/sec
   C) 0.5 mi/min   D) 30 mi/sec

2) A store at Elmwood Mall sells 6 bicycles each day. How many bicycles do they sell in 32 weeks?

   A) 1,344 bicycles   B) 224 bicycles
   C) 192 bicycles   D) 1,280 bicycles

3) Solve.
   At the Shirt Company, $686 in daily income comes from T-shirt sales. How much income is made from T-shirt sales in a 30-day period?

Section 7C Similarity

7-8   Creating and Exploring Similar Figures

1) $\triangle ABC \sim \triangle DEF$. If $m\angle B = 26°$, what is the measurement of the corresponding angle in $\triangle DEF$?

   A) 26°   B) 116°   C) 64°   D) 154°

2) $\triangle ABC \sim \triangle DEF$. If $m\angle A = 42°$, $m\angle B = 56°$, $m\angle C = 82°$, find $m\angle F$, $m\angle E$, and $m\angle D$.

3) Tell whether the two figures are similar. If they are, write a similarity statement using $\sim$ and give the scale factor. If they are not, explain why not.

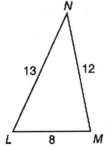

4) Tell whether the two figures are similar. If they are, write a similarity statement using ~ and give the scale factor. If they are not similar, explain why.

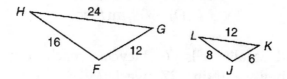

7-9   Finding Measures of Similar Figures

1) The scale factor of two squares is 4. The larger square has a side measuring 32 ft. what is the measurement of a side of the smaller square?

A) 8 ft   B) 16 ft   C) 24 ft   D) 4 ft

2) Solve.
The scale factor for two squares is 6. The smaller square has a side measuring 24 ft. What is the measurement of a side of the larger square?

3) $\triangle ABC \sim \triangle DEF$. Find x.

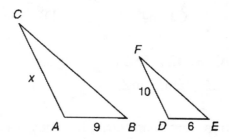

4) A person who is 4 feet tall casts a shadow 5 feet long. How tall is a flagpole that casts a shadow 28.5 feet long?

A) 19 ft   B) 18.8 ft   C) 22.8 ft   D) 21.2 ft

5) When an oak tree's shadow is 6 feet long, an aspen tree's shadow is 10.8 feet long. If the oak tree is 40 feet tall, how tall is the aspen?

6) A pole that is 8 feet tall casts a shadow that is 6 feet long. How long is the shadow cast by a nearby tree that is 40 feet tall?

A) 60 ft   B) 120 ft   C) 80 ft   D) 30 ft

7–10 Perimeters and Areas of Similar Figures

1) The scale factor of two similar figures is 6. The perimeter of the smaller figure is 30 in. What is the perimeter of the larger figure?

2) The scale factor of two similar figures is 5. The area of the larger figure is 350 in^2. What is the area of the smaller figure?

A) 14 in^2

B) 70 in^2

C) 15 in^2

D) 1,750 in^2

3) Two rectangles are similar with scale factor 6. The smaller rectangle has a perimeter of 52 cm and an area of 168 cm^2. Find the perimeter and area of the larger rectangle.

4) The scale factor of two similar figures is 6. The area of the larger figure is 288 m^2. What is the area of the smaller figure?

A) 24 m^2 B) 16 m^2 C) 8 m^2 D) 48 m^2

Chapter 7 Proportion, Scale, and Similarity

Section 7A Scale Drawings, Maps, and Scales

7-1   Measurement: Estimating Actual and Scale Distances

1)   Answer: B

2)   Answer: D

3)   Answer: 1.5 in.

4)   Answer: C

5)   Answer: A

6)   Answer: C

7-2   Calculating with Scales

1)   Answer: D

2)   Answer: B

3)   Answer: a. 1 in.   b. 20 ft

7-3   Problem Solving Using Maps

1)   Answer: C

2)   Answer: C

3)   Answer: A

7-4   Creating Scale Drawings and Scale Models

1)   Answer: C

2)   Answer: A

3)   Answer: D

Section 7B Dimensional Analysis

7-5   Choosing Appropriate Rates and Units

1)   Answer: Possible answer: mi/hr

2)   Answer: Possible answer: cents/pound

3)   Answer: Possible answer: in./hr

4)   Answer: C

5)   Answer: C

6)   Answer: 435

7-6   Converting Units

1)   Answer: C

2)   Answer: A

3)   Answer: $10/ft

7-7   Problem Solving   Converting Rates

1)   Answer: B

2)   Answer: A

3)   Answer: $20,580

Section 7C Similarity

7-8   Creating and Exploring Similar Figures

1)   Answer: A

2)   Answer: $m\angle F = 82°$, $m\angle E = 56°$, $m\angle D = 42°$

3)   Answer:

The figures are not similar, because the lengths of the corresponding sides do not have equal ratios.

4)   Answer: $\triangle FGH \sim \triangle JKL$; Scale factor is $\dfrac{2}{1}$

7-9   Finding Measures of Similar Figures

1)   Answer: A

2)   Answer: 144 ft

3)   Answer: $x = 15$

4)   Answer: C

5)   Answer: 72 ft

6)   Answer: D

7–10 Perimeters and Areas of Similar Figures

1)   Answer: 180 in.

2)   Answer: A

3)   Answer: Perimeter = 312 cm, area = 6,048 cm^2

4)   Answer: C

Chapter 8 Percents

Section 8A Understanding and Estimating Percents

8-1   Understanding Percents

1)   Express 16 nickels as a percent of a dollar.

    A) 1.6%   B) 80%   C) 32%   D) 16%

2)   Express 3 quarters as a percent of a dollar.

    A) 50%   B) 60%   C) 75%   D) 70%

3)   Convert to percents and determine which one of these is the greatest.

    A) $\dfrac{19}{25}$ B) $\dfrac{47}{100}$ C) $\dfrac{17}{20}$ D) $\dfrac{6}{10}$

4)   Convert to percents and determine which one of these is the least: $\dfrac{25}{50}$, $\dfrac{2}{5}$, $\dfrac{7}{20}$, and $\dfrac{39}{100}$.

    A) $\dfrac{25}{50}$ B) $\dfrac{7}{20}$ C) $\dfrac{39}{100}$ D) $\dfrac{2}{5}$

5)   Express each ratio as a percent. Then compare the ratios using the symbol <, >, or =.
$\dfrac{18}{50}$ and $\dfrac{14}{20}$

8-2   Linking Fractions, Decimals, and Percents

1)   What percent is equal to $\dfrac{11}{20}$?

    A) 55%   B) 22%   C) 110%   D) 11%

2) Write 0.48 as a percent and a fraction in lowest terms.

A) $0.48\%; \dfrac{0.48}{100}$

B) $48\%; \dfrac{12}{25}$

C) $0.48\%; \dfrac{12}{25}$

D) $4.8\%; \dfrac{6}{25}$

3) Write 0.31 as a percent and a fraction in lowest terms.

4) In Alta, $\dfrac{3}{25}$ of the trees are aspen trees. Express this fraction as a percent.

A) 6%   B) 12%   C) 120%   D) 5%

5) The decimal 1.028 is equal to what percent?

A) 10.28%   B) 1.028%   C) 102.8%   D) 1,028%

6) Which of the following is equal to 718%

A) $\dfrac{71.8}{100}$ B) $\dfrac{359}{500}$ C) 7.18   D) 0.718

7) Write $\dfrac{49}{7}$ as a percent.

A) 700%   B) 7%   C) 70%   D) 0.7%

8–3   Percents Greater than 100 or Less than 1

1) Which of the following correctly describes 0.245?

A) Less than 1%   B) Between 1% and 100%
C) Greater than 100%   D) Not here

2) Which of the following correctly describes 3.56?

A) Less than 1%   B) Greater than 100%
C) Between 1% and 100%   D) Not here

3) Which of the following correctly describes 0.569?

    A) Greater than 100%   B) Between 1% and 100%
    C) Less than 1%   D) Not here

4) Write each decimal or fraction as a percent.

    a. 0.0946 _____

    b. $\dfrac{3}{2000}$ _____

5) Write 0.0085 as a percent.

    A) 0.000085%   B) 0.85%   C) 8.5%   D) 0.085%

6) Which of the following correctly describes 3.734?

    A) Between 1% and 100%   B) Less than 1%
    C) Greater than 100%   D) Not here

7) Which of the following correctly describes $\dfrac{68}{42}$?

    A) Greater than 100%   B) Less than 1%
    C) Between 1% and 100%   D) Not here

8) Classify each decimal as a percent that is less than 1%, greater than 100%, or between 1% and 100%.

    a. 1.653 _____

    b. 3.021 _____

9) Write 5.2 as a percent.

    A) 52%   B) 520%   C) 0.052%   D) 0.52%

8-4 Finding a Percent of a Number Mentally

1) Use mental math to solve.

   20% of 68

2) Use mental math to solve.

   50% of 84

3) Use mental math to solve.

   50% of 48

4) Use mental math to solve.

   20% of 48

5) Use mental math to solve.

   20% of 68

6) Use mental math to solve.

   90% of 90

Section 8B Problem Solving with Percents

8-5 Using Equations to Solve Percent Problems

1) What percent of 85 is 51?

   A) 45%   B) 70%   C) 60%   D) 55%

2) 85% of 46 is what number?

   A) 41.9   B) 36.3   C) 39.1   D) 38.6

3) What percent of 84 is 30?

   A) 300%   B) 31.4%   C) 24.6%   D) 35.7%

4) 28% of what number is 91?

A) 273.1   B) 269.2   C) 325   D) 321.4

5) What percent of 650 is 416?

6) Solve.
40% of 70 is what number?

7) Solve.
7% of 32 is what number?

8-6 Solving Percent Problems with Proportions

1) Solve.
349 is 49% of what number? Your answer should be rounded to the nearest tenth.

2) Solve.
366 is what percent of 488?

3) What number do you get when 48 is increased by 75%?

A) 36   B) 60   C) 72   D) 84

4) What number do you get when 85 is decreased by 70%?

A) 18.5   B) 35.5   C) 25.5   D) 59.5

5) 925 is what percent of 625?

A) 130%   B) 148%   C) 150%   D) 30%

6) Solve.
Students bought 23 out of 87 models at the museum store. What percent, rounded to the nearest tenth, of the models did they buy?

7) Solve.
In a shipment of medical tools, 5% were defective. If 12 of the tools were defective, how many medical tools were in the shipment?

A) 60   B) 360   C) 120   D) 240

8-7 Problem Solving   Percent Increase and Decrease

1) What is the total cost of a backpack priced at $54.80 if there is a 6% sales tax?

A) $54.86   B) $57.29   C) $58.09   D) $57.99

2) Solve.
A stereo system that previously sold for $1200 has been marked down to $900. What is the percent of decrease?

3) Solve.
The troop hoped to raise $90. They raised $180. What percent of their goal did they raise?

4) What is the total cost of lunch if the check is for $12.74 and you want to leave a 15% tip?

5) What is the selling price of a tent that has a list price of $178.89 if a 20% discount is offered?

6) Solve.
The cost of admission for a class at the planetarium increased by 8%. The new cost is $64.80. What was the admission cost before the increase?

7) Solve.
A bicycle that previously sold for $190 has been marked down to $133. What is the percent of decrease?

Chapter 8 Percents

Section 8A Understanding and Estimating Percents

8-1 Understanding Percents

1)   Answer: B

2)   Answer: C

3)   Answer: C

4)   Answer: B

5)   Answer: 36% < 70%

8-2 Linking Fractions, Decimals, and Percents

1)   Answer: A

2)   Answer: B

3)   Answer: $31\%; \dfrac{31}{100}$

4)   Answer: B

5)   Answer: C

6)   Answer: C

7)   Answer: A

8-3 Percents Greater than 100 or Less than 1

1)   Answer: B

2)   Answer: B

3)   Answer: B

4)   Answer: a. 9.46%

             b. 0.0015%

5)   Answer: B

6)   Answer: C

7)   Answer: A

8)   Answer: a. greater than 100%

b. greater than 100%

9)   Answer: B

8-4   Finding a Percent of a Number Mentally
1)   Answer: 13.6

2)   Answer: 42

3)   Answer: 24

4)   Answer: 9.6

5)   Answer: 13.6

6)   Answer: 81

Section 8B Problem Solving with Percents
8-5   Using Equations to Solve Percent Problems
1)   Answer: C

2)   Answer: C

3)   Answer: D

4)   Answer: C

5)   Answer: 64%

6)   Answer: 28

7)   Answer: 2.24

8-6   Solving Percent Problems with Proportions
1)   Answer: 712.2

2)   Answer: 75%

3)   Answer: D

4)   Answer: C

5)   Answer: B

6)   Answer: 26.4%

7)   Answer: D

8-7   Problem Solving   Percent Increase and Decrease

1)   Answer: C

2)   Answer: 25%

3)   Answer: 200%

4)   Answer: $14.65

5)   Answer: $143.11

6)   Answer: $60

7)   Answer: 30%

Chapter 9 Integers

Section 9A Using Integers

9-1 Using Integers to Represent Quantities

1) Use a sign to write the number.
   A net gain of $35

2) Use a sign to write the number.
   A net gain of 121 points

3) Keisha lost $420 on a stock investment. What integer represents her loss?
   A) 420   B) –995.8   C) –420%   D) –420

4) Use a sign to write the number.
   A net profit of $56
   A) –56%   B) +$56   C) –$56   D) +56%

5) Use a sign to write the number.
   190 feet below sea level.
   A) +190%   B) +190 feet
   C) –190 feet   D) –190%

6) Use a sign to write the number.
   A football team lost 6 yards on one play.

7) Which of the following represents 485 feet above sea level?
   A) –485   B) 485%
   C) 485   D) 48.5 × 100

8) Write the opposite of –24.
   A) 24   B) –24   C) $-|24|$ D) 2.4

9) Write the opposite of 3.

10) Write the opposite of 0.
    A) 1   B) 0
    C) –1   D) Not here

11) Write the opposite of 74.
   A) –74   B) 74   C) –148   D) | –74 |

12) Write the opposite of $-\frac{1}{7}$.

   A) $\frac{1}{7}$ B) 71   C) 17   D) 7

13) Which of the following represents the opposite of 98?
   A) 89   B) –98   C) | –98 | D) 98

14) Write the opposite of –304.
   A) –30.4   B) 304   C) –304   D) 30.4

15) Write the opposite of 112.
   A) | –112 | B) –112   C) 112   D) –1,120

16) What is the absolute value of –72?
   A) –| 72 | B) 72   C) 0   D) –72

17) | 141 | is equal to what value?
   A) 141   B) –141   C) –| 141 | D) 0

18) Write the value: | –26 | = _____
   A) –| 26 | B) –26   C) –| –26 | D) 26

19) What is the absolute value of 18?
   A) 18   B) –| 18 | C) –| –18 | D) –18

20) Use absolute value signs to write the absolute value of negative 82.

21) Which of the following represents the absolute value of –79?

   A) | –79 | B) –1 × | 79 |
   C) –| 79 | D) Not here

22) Find the absolute value of | –1,522 |.

23) What is the absolute value of 0?
  A) 0   B) −1   C) 1   D) $|-1|$

9-2 Comparing and Ordering Integers

1) Use <, >, or = to compare −14 and −13.

2) Use <, >, or = to compare $|-59|$ and $|7|$.

3) Order the numbers from least to greatest.
  9, −27, −18, 0, 27

4) Order the numbers from least to greatest.
  −22, 0, 26, 22, −26

5) Which of the following is true?
  A) −36 > −37   B) $|-36|$ < −37
  C) $|-36|$ > $|-37|$ D) Not here

6) Which integer is the greatest: 530, −532, 531, $|530|$?

  A) 530   B) 531   C) $|530|$ D) −532

7) Which integer is least: −35, $|-87|$, 27, 0?

  A) 0   B) −35   C) 27   D) $|-87|$

9-3 The Coordinate Plane

1) In which quadrant is the point C(2, 3)?

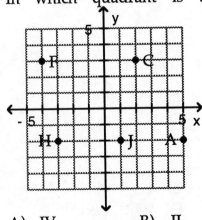

  A) IV   B) II   C) III   D) I

2)   Which point is at (–2, 2)?

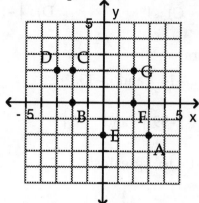

A) Point F   B) Point C   C) Point D   D) Point E

3)   Find the coordinates of point G.

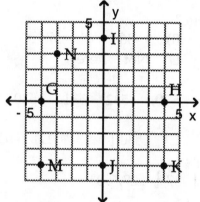

A) (0, –4)   B) (0, 4)   C) (–4, 0)   D) (4, 0)

4)   Find the coordinates of point D.

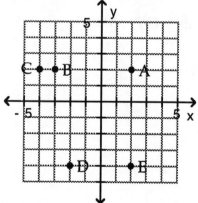

A) (–2, 4)   B) (2, –4)
C) (–2, –4)   D) Not here

5)   Find the coordinates of each point.
       a. A
       b. B
       c. C

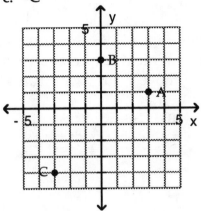

6)   Name the axis that contains the point (0, –4).

7)   Which point is at (3, –2)?

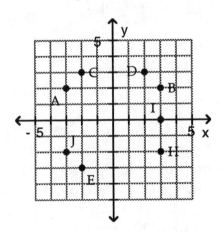

Section 9B Operations with Integers

9–4   Adding Integers

1)   Find the sum of –38 + 63.

2)   Find the sum of –67 + 37.
       A) 30   B) 104   C) –104   D) –30

3)   Find the sum of 47 + –64.

4) A football team lost 5 yards on one play and lost 23 on the next play. Express this situation as an addition of integers, and find the sum.

5) Solve.
In a board game, Kim moves ahead 6 squares. Then he has to move back 8 squares. Which expression shows the total number of squares Kim moves in two turns?

A) –6 + 8   B) –6 + (–8)
C) (–8) + (–6)   D) 6 + (–8)

6) Find the sum –98 + (–54).
A) 152   B) –44   C) 44   D) –152

7) Solve.
A player moves 5 spaces forward on a game board. On the next play she goes back 2 spaces. What was her change in position on the board after the 2 plays?

A) –3 spaces   B) 3 spaces
C) 7 spaces   D) –7 spaces

8) Solve.
Dennis had 40 points after 3 rounds in a card game. He lost a certain number of points in the fourth round, which resulted in a new score of –20 points. Which of the following represents the change in his point total?

A) 20 points   B) –20 points
C) –60 points   D) –50 points

9–5 Subtracting Integers

1) Find the difference.
45 – 99

A) –144   B) –54   C) 54   D) 144

2) Find the difference.
–48 – 67

©Addison Wesley Longman, Inc.

3)   Find the difference.
     237 – (–408)

     A) –645   B) –171   C) 171   D) 645

4)   Find the difference.
     –490 – 97

     A) 587   B) 393   C) –587   D) –393

5)   Solve.
     A ski lift has an elevation change of 350 feet from a mountain top. A new route will have a change of –125 feet from that same mountain top. What is the difference in change between the 2 routes?

     A) 350 – 125   B) –125 – (–350)
     C) –125 – 350   D) 350 – (–125)

6)   Solve.
     A submarine was at 150 feet below see level before diving an additional 230 feet. Express this situation as a subtraction of integers and find the change new position of the submarine.

7)   Solve.
     At its lowest, the elevation of Death Valley is –282 ft. At its highest, the elevation of Mount Whitney is 14,494 ft. Find the change in elevation from Death Valley to the top of Mt. Whitney.

9–6   Multiplying Integers

1)   Find the product.
     29 × –7

     A) 36   B) 22   C) 203   D) –203

2)   Find the product.
     50 × 50

     A) 2,500   B) –50   C) 0   D) –2,500

3) Find the product.
−69 × 8

   A) −552   B) 77   C) 552   D) −77

4) Find the product.
−98 × −27

5) Solve.
Kara earned an average of $12 each week for 6 weeks. Which expression shows the change in her earnings?

   A) $72 \times \dfrac{1}{6}$ B) $12 \times \dfrac{1}{6}$

   C) 12×6 D) $\dfrac{1}{12} \times \dfrac{1}{6}$

6) Solve.
During a 4-day heat wave, an amusement park reported an average change in income of −$38,000 per day. Find the total change in income during that time period?

7) Solve.
At Crescent Parks and Recreation, the average change in baseball sign ups was −35 per year during the last 7 years. Which of the following represents the change in sign ups during that time period?

   A) 245 players   B) 5 players
   C) −5 players   D) −245 players

8) Find the product 6 × (−40).

9–7 Dividing Integers

1) Find the quotient.
−33 ÷ 1.

   A) −33   B) |−33| C) 1   D) 33

2) Find the quotient.
    40 ÷ 10.

    A) 4   B) –|4|
    C) –4   D) Not here

3) Find the quotient.
    720 ÷ –8

4) Find the quotient –345 ÷ (–15).

    A) –360   B) –330   C) 23   D) –23

5) Find the quotient –448 ÷ 32.

    A) 14   B) –416   C) –14   D) 416

6) Solve.
    A climber descends from the mouth of a cave (0
    meters) to –240 meters in 4 minutes. What was the
    change in elevation per minute?

    A) -960 m   B) –236 m   C) –60 m   D) –244 m

7) Solve.
    The temperature changed –32 degrees Fahrenheit in 8
    hours. Find the average change in termperature per hour.

Chapter 9 Integers

Section 9A Using Integers

9-1   Using Integers to Represent Quantities

1)   Answer: +$35

2)   Answer: +121   points

3)   Answer: D

4)   Answer: B

5)   Answer: C

6)   Answer: –6   yards

7)   Answer: C

8)   Answer: A

9)   Answer: –3

10)   Answer: B

11)   Answer: A

12)   Answer: A

13)   Answer: B

14)   Answer: B

15)   Answer: B

16)   Answer: B

17)   Answer: A

18)   Answer: D

19)   Answer: A

20)   Answer: |–82|

21)   Answer: A

22)   Answer: 1,522

23)   Answer: A

9–2   Comparing and Ordering Integers

1)   Answer: –14 < –13

2)   Answer: |–59| > |7|

3)   Answer: –27, –18, 0, 9, 27

4)   Answer: –26, –22, 0, 22, 26

5)   Answer: A

6)   Answer: B

7)   Answer: B

9–3   The Coordinate Plane

1)   Answer: D

2)   Answer: B

3)   Answer: C

4)   Answer: C

5)   Answer: a.   (3,   1)
                 b.   (0,   3)
                 c.   (–3,   –4)

6)   Answer: y–axis

7)   Answer: Point H

Section 9B Operations with Integers

9–4   Adding Integers

1)   Answer: 25

2)   Answer: D

3)   Answer: –17

4)   Answer: –5 + (–23) = –28

5)   Answer: D

6)   Answer: D

7)   Answer: B

8)   Answer: C

9–5   Subtracting Integers

1)   Answer: B

2)   Answer: –115

3)   Answer: D

4)   Answer: C

5)   Answer: D

6)   Answer: –150 – 230 = –380, 380 feet below sea level

7)   Answer: 14,776 ft

9–6   Multiplying Integers

1)   Answer: D

2)   Answer: A

3)   Answer: A

4)   Answer: 2,646

5)   Answer: C

6)   Answer: –$152,000

7)   Answer: D

8)   Answer: –240

9–7   Dividing Integers

1)   Answer: A

2)   Answer: A

3)   Answer: –90

4)   Answer: C

5)   Answer: C

6)   Answer: C

7)   Answer: –4   degrees   Fahrenheit

Chapter 10 The Patterns of Algebra: Equations and Graphs

10A Tables, Equations, and Graphs

10-1 Quantities, Constants, and Variables

1) Is the number of hours in a day a variable or a constant?

2) Which of the following is *not* a variable: the weight of a watermelon, the number of pints in a quart, the cost to make a movie, or the sounds a bird makes?

   A) weight of a watermelon
   B) cost to make a movie
   C) sounds a bird makes
   D) number of pints in a quart

3) Is the number of feet in a yard a variable or a constant?

10-2 Relating Graphs to Stories

1) Solve.
   You are swimming in a lake at a constant speed. Graph the story that relates the time to the distance traveled.

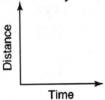

2)   Which graph shows the distance traveled by a climber climbing at a steady speed until stopping for a rest at the peak?

A)

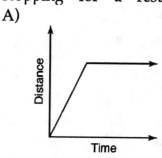

B)

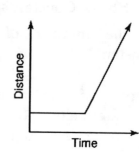

C)

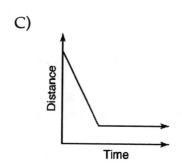

D)

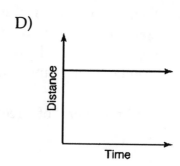

3)   Solve.

A student leaves home and walks to the library at a steady rate. He reads a magazine at the library, then walks home at a steady rate. Graph the story that relates his distance from home to the time.

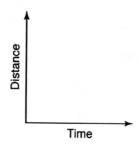

4) Which of the following stories is represented by the graph below?

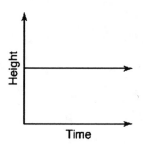

A) The height of an airplane during takeoff
B) The height of an airplane taking off and then flying at a constant altitude
C) The height of an airplane during landing
D) The height of an airplane flying at a constant altitude

5) The graph shows the amount of fuel in an automobile over time. Tell a story that fits the graph.

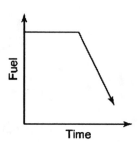

6) Which of the following fits the graph below?

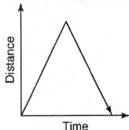

A) Distance covered by a skier skiing down a mountain at a constant rate.
B) Distance up the mountain of a hiker climbing to the summit at a steady rate.
C) Distance covered by a train traveling at a steady rate from the country to the city.
D) Distance from home of a hiker hiking at a constant rate on a round trip.

10-3 Tables and Expressions

1) What rule describes this sequence?

Term Number (n)	1	2	3	4	5
Number in Sequence	4	8	12	16	20

A) 4n B) 8n C) 20n D) 12n

2) What rule describes this sequence?

Term Number (n)	1	2	3	4	5
Number in Sequence	6	7	8	9	10

A) n + 9 B) n + 5 C) n + 6 D) n + 7

3) Write an expression describing the rule for this sequence. Then give the 12th term.

Term Number (n)	1	2	3	4	5
Number in Sequence	$\frac{1}{5}$	$\frac{2}{5}$	$\frac{3}{5}$	$\frac{4}{5}$	1

4) Is the sequence 2, 3, 5, 6 . . . arithmetic, geometric, or neither? Give the next term.

A) neither, 8
B) geometric, 16
C) arithmetic, 144
D) neither, 144

5) Tell whether the sequence $\frac{3}{4}$, 3, 12, 48 . . . arithmetic, geometric, or neither? Give the next term.

6) Tell whether the sequence 1, 5, 9, 13, . . . is arithmetic, geometric, or neither. Give the next term.

10-4 Understanding and Writing Equations

1) What equation shows the relationship between x and y?

x	8	3	10	4
y	18	23	16	22

A) y = 26 – x
B) y = x + 26
C) y = x + 25
D) y = 25 – x

2) What equation shows the relationship between x and y?

x	6	12	18	24
y	2	4	6	8

A) y = x/3
B) y = x + 6
C) y = x + 4
D) y = x/6

3) What equation shows the relationship between x and y?

x	5	10	15	20
y	2	7	12	17

A) $y = x + 5$ B) $y = x - 4$
C) $y = x - 3$ D) $y = x/5$

10-5 Equations and Graphs

1) Complete the table for $y = x + 7$.

x	y
-1	
0	
1	
2	
3	

2) Use the table of points to graph the equation:
$y = x - 2$

x	y
-1	-3
0	-2
2	0
3	1
4	2

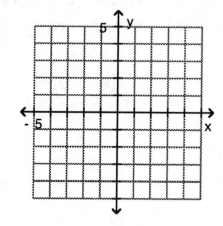

3)   Use the table of points to graph the equation:
      $y = -2x + 1$

x	y
−2	5
−1	3
0	1
1	−1
2	−3

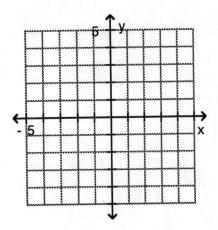

4)   Graph the equation: $y = 3x + 2$

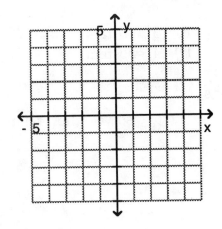

10B Understanding Equations

10–6   Solving Equations Using Tables

1)   The table was created from the equation $y = 6x - 4$.
      Use it to solve $-4 = 6x - 4$

x	0	1	2	3	4
y	−4	2	8	14	20

A) $x = -4$ B) $x = 8$ C) $x = 0$ D) $x = 20$

2) The table was created from the equation $y = 3x + 3$. Use it to solve $9 = 3x + 3$

x	0	2	4	6	8
y	3	9	15	21	27

A) $x = -2$ B) $x = 9$ C) $x = 15$ D) $x = 2$

3) Solve.
Tanner designs posters for special events. He charges an overall fee of $24 in addition to a $6 per poster fee. Use the table to find how many posters he made if he was paid $42 for an order.

x	1	2	3	4	5
y	30	36	42	48	54

A) 5 posters   B) 3 posters
C) 2 posters   D) 4 posters

10–7 Solving Equations Using Graphs

1) Use the graph of $y = 2x - 1$ to solve the related equation $1 = 2x - 1$.

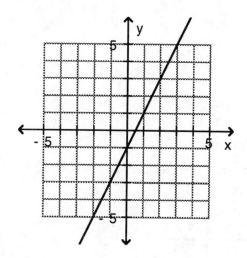

A) $x = 1$ B) $x = 2$ C) $x = -1$ D) $x = 0$

2) Use the graph of $y = 4x + 5$ to solve the related equation $-3 = 4x + 5$.

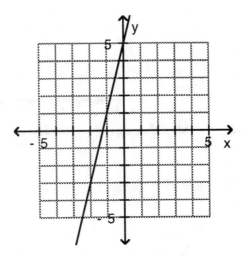

A) $x = 2$ B) $x = 1$ C) $x = -2$ D) $x = -1$

3) Use the graph of $y = 2x - 3$ to solve the related equation $-3 = 2x - 3$.

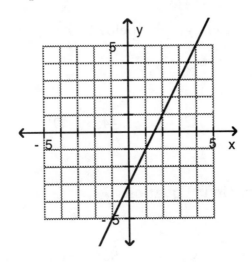

10–8   Relating Equations and Inequalities

1) Graph $x \geq 3$ on a number line.

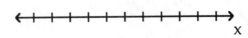

2) Graph x < 6 on a number line.

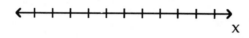

x

3) Which is the graph of y > –2?

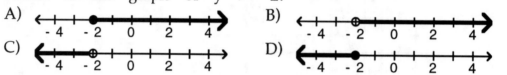

4) Write the inequality for the graph.

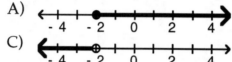

5) What inequality represents the graph below?

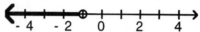

A) x > 5   B) x < 5   C) x ≥ 5   D) x ≤ 5

6) What inequality represents the graph below?

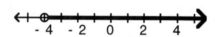

A) y < –4   B) y > –4   C) y ≥ –4   D) y ≤ –4

10C Integer Equations

10–9 Integer Addition and Subtraction Equations

1) Solve the equation. a + 31 = –59

A) a = –90   B) a = 93   C) a = 90   D) a = –93

2) Solve the equation. m – 35 = –25

A) m = –13   B) m = –60
C) m = 10   D) m = 60

3) Solve the equation. c + 14 = –6

A) c = –23   B) c = 20   C) c = –20   D) c = 23

4)   Solve the equation. $y - (-20) = -75$

10–10 Integer Multiplication and Division Equations

1)   Solve the equation. $\frac{d}{3} = -24$

    A) d = –72   B) d = 8
    C) d = 72   D) d = –8

2)   Solve the equation. $-7k = -63$

    A) k = –9   B) k = –441
    C) k = 441   D) k = 9

3)   Solve the equation. $8 = 24r$

    A) r = 3   B) r = –3
    C) r = 0.33333333   D) r = –0.3333333

4)   Solve the equation. $1 = \frac{f}{5}$

10–11 Solving Two–Step Equations

1)   Solve the equation.
        $7 = 8w + 39$

        A) w = 4   B) w = –4   C) w = –3   D) w = 3

2)   Solve the equation. $3 = \frac{n}{3} - 8$

3)   Solve the equation. $10p - 9 = -94$

4)   Solve the equation. $\frac{i}{3} - 8 = 0$

10-12 Problem Solving with Integer Equations

1) Solve.

Jared wants to buy a guitar that costs $480. He will be able to save $12 per week in order to buy it. How many weeks will pass before he can buy the guitar?

A) 80 weeks

B) 120 weeks

C) 5,760 weeks

D) 40 weeks

2) Solve.

Marta has 15 party favors. This amount is $\frac{1}{4}$ the number of favors that she needs for her party. How many party favors does Marta need?

3) Solve.

The amount of snow accumulation changes $-3\frac{1}{4}$ inches to $12\frac{1}{2}$ inches. What was the amount of snow before the change?

A) $9\frac{3}{4}$ inches

B) $15\frac{3}{4}$ inches

C) $16\frac{1}{4}$ inches

D) $9\frac{1}{4}$ inches

Chapter 10 The Patterns of Algebra: Equations and Graphs

10A Tables, Equations, and Graphs

10-1   Quantities, Constants, and Variables

1)   Answer: constant

2)   Answer: D

3)   Answer: constant

10-2   Relating Graphs to Stories

1)   Answer: Possible   answer:

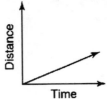

2)   Answer: A

3)   Answer:

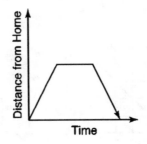

4)   Answer: D

5)   Answer: Possible   answer: The   car   was   stopped   and   then   when   driven   used   fuel   at   a   constant   rate.

6)   Answer: D

10-3   Tables and Expressions

1)   Answer: A

2)   Answer: B

3)   Answer: $\dfrac{n}{5}$; $2\dfrac{2}{5}$

4)   Answer: A

5)   Answer: geometric, 192

6)   Answer: arithmetic, 17

10–4   Understanding and Writing Equations

1)   Answer: A

2)   Answer: A

3)   Answer: C

10–5   Equations and Graphs

1)   Answer:

x	y
–1	6
0	7
1	8
2	9
3	10

2)   Answer:

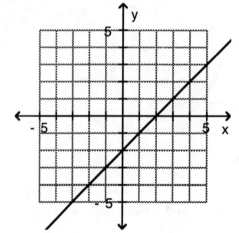

3)   Answer:

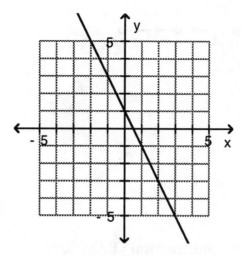

4)   Answer:

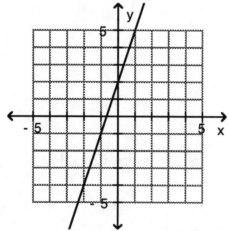

10B Understanding Equations

10–6   Solving Equations Using Tables

1)   Answer: C

2)   Answer: D

3)   Answer: B

10–7   Solving Equations Using Graphs

1)   Answer: A

2)   Answer: C

3)   Answer: $x = 0$

10–8   Relating Equations and Inequalities

1)   Answer:

2) Answer:

3) Answer: B

4) Answer: x < -1

5) Answer: B

6) Answer: B

10C Integer Equations

10-9 Integer Addition and Subtraction Equations

1) Answer: A

2) Answer: C

3) Answer: C

4) Answer: $y = -95$

10-10 Integer Multiplication and Division Equations

1) Answer: A

2) Answer: D

3) Answer: C

4) Answer: $f = 5$

10-11 Solving Two-Step Equations

1) Answer: B

2) Answer: $n = 33$

3) Answer: $p = -8.5$

4) Answer: $i = 24$

10-12 Problem Solving with Integer Equations

1) Answer: D

2) Answer: 60 party favors

3) Answer: B

©Addison Wesley Longman, Inc.

Chapter 11 Geometry

11A Polyhedrons

11-1 Exploring Polyhedrons

1) Name the polyhedron.

A) Square pyramid   B) Triangular pyramid
C) Cone   D) Cube

2) Name the polyhedron.

A) Triangular pyramid   B) Cube
C) Rectangular pyramid   D) Triangular prism

3) Name the polyhedron.

_____

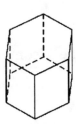

A) Rectangular prism   B) Triangular prism
C) Hexagonal prism   D) Pentagonal prism

4) Sketch a pentagonal pyramid in the space below.

5) Sketch a rectangular prism in the space below.

6) What are the bases of a prism shaped like?

A) Points   B) Polygons   C) Pyramids   D) Circles

11-2 Isometric and Orthographic Drawing

1) Which of these is a set of orthographic views for the isometric drawing below?

A)
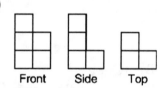

B)
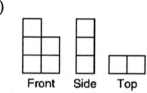

C)
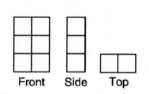

D)
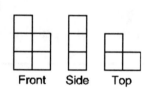

2) Sketch a set of orthographic views from the isometric drawing below.

    Front   Side   Top

3) Sketch a set of orthographic views from the isometric drawing below.

Front   Side   Top

4) Sketch front, side and top views for the figure.

Front   Side   Top

5) Which of these is a top view of the figure?

A)

B)

C)

D)

6) Which of these is a side view of the figure?

A)   B)   C)   D)

7) Which of these is a perspective sketch of the object?

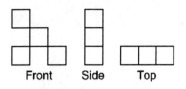
Front   Side   Top

A)    B) 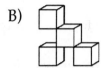   C) 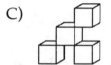   D)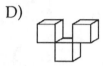

8) Which of these is a perspective sketch of the object?

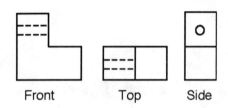
Front   Top   Side

A) 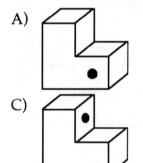   B)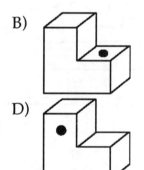

C)   D)

9) Make a perspective sketch of the object below.

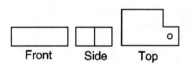
Front   Side   Top

11-3 Polyhedron Nets and Surface Areas

1) What is the surface area of a cube with the dimensions of
9 m × 9 m by 9 m

A) 729 m^2 B) 324 m^2 C) 486 m^2 D) 405 m^2

2) Ryan is making a cardboard model shaped like a rectangular prism. How much cardboard will he need to make all sides of a prism that is 10 cm long, 2 cm wide, and 8 cm high?

A) 320 cm^2 B) 116 cm^2 C) 160 cm^2 D) 232 cm^2

3) Sheri has a box in the shape of a triangular prism that she wants to paint for a gift. The triangular base is 5 cm by 12 cm by 13 cm (there is a right angle between the 5 cm-side and 12 cm sides). The prism is 4 cm high. Find how much paint Sheri will need if she wants to cover the entire prism.

A) 3,120 cm^2 B) 6,240 cm^2
C) 132 cm^2 D) 180 cm^2

11-4 Volumes of Prisms

1) What is the volume of a cube with dimensions 8 m × 8 m × 8 m?

A) 1,024 m^3 B) 64 m^3 C) 512 m^3 D) 128 m^3

2) Solve.
Mike wants to fill a box that is shaped like a rectangular prism. It is 8 in. long, 4 in. wide, and 4 in. high. How much room is there in the box?

A) 256 in^3 B) 128 in^3 C) 160 in^3 D) 80 in^3

3) Solve.
Marta made a triangular prism out of glass. The triangular base was 10 cm by 24 cm by 26 cm (there is a right angle between the 10-cm side and 24-cm sides). The prism is 3 cm high. She wants to fill the prism with colored water. How much water will it hold?

A) 360 cm^3 B) 6,240 cm^3
C) 720 cm^3 D) 3,120 cm^3

11B Circles and Cylinders

11-5 Circles and Circle Graphs

1) Use the circle graph to estimate what percent of Kaden's diet is fruits and vegetables.

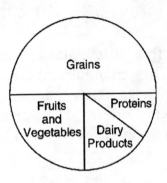

A) about 15%

B) about 25%

C) about 50%

D) about 10%

2) Solve.
Amy is making a circle graph. She wants to mark an area to show that 80% of the money she earns is put in savings. What central angle will show this?

A) 72°   B) 288°   C) 144°   D) 216°

3) Solve.
Scott made the circle graph below to show the percent of the days in his city that are sunny and the percent of the days that are rainy. What central angle did he use to show how many rainy days there were?

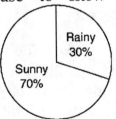

A) 144°   B) 108°   C) 126°   D) 90°

11–6 Pi and Circumference

1) For which measurement of a circle would you most likely use π?

A) Circumference   B) Chord
C) Length   D) Diameter

2) The distance across a circle is 7 in. Using $\frac{22}{7}$ for π, find the distance around the same circle.

A) 22 in.   B) 27 in.   C) 26 in.   D) 25 in.

3) How are π, a circle's diameter (d), and a circle's circumference (C) related? Express the relationship in a formula.

A) $C = \pi d$

B) $C = \pi r$

C) $C = \pi \cdot 2d$

D) $C = \pi \frac{d}{2}$

4) Find the circumference of a circle with diameter 12 m. Use 3.14 for π.

A) 40.82 m   B) 37.68 m   C) 18.84 m   D) 75.36 m

5) Find the circumference of a circle with radius 8 ft. Use 3.14 for π. Round the answer to the nearest tenth.

A) 50.2 ft   B) 25.1 ft   C) 100.5 ft   D) 12.6 ft

6) There is a circular field with a diameter of 42 yd. Find the distance around the field. Use $\frac{22}{7}$ for π.

A) 66 yd   B) 264 yd   C) 126 yd   D) 132 yd

11-7 Area of a Circle

1) Find the area of a circle with diameter 8 ft. Use 3.14 for π.

    A) 25.12 ft^2 B) 50.24 ft^2
    C) 12.56 ft^2 D) 200.96 ft^2

2) Find the area of a circle with radius 3 km. Use 3.14 for π . Round the answer to the nearest tenth.

    A) 18.84 km^2 B) 28.26 km^2
    C) 9.42 km^2 D) 56.52 km^2

3) There is a circular stadium with a diameter of 70 m. Find how much land the stadium covers. Use $\dfrac{22}{7}$ for π.

11-8 Surface Areas of Cylinders

1) Find the surface area of a can with a diameter of 8 in. and a height of 6 in. Use 3.14 for π.

    A) 75.36 in^2 B) 119.32 in^2
    C) 251.20 in^2 D) 100.48 in^2

2) Solve.
John has a case shaped like a cylinder. It has a radius of 3 cm and a height of 7 cm. Find how much foil John will need to cover the case. Use 3.14 for π. Round to the nearest tenth.

    A) 452.16 cm^2 B) 150.7 cm^2
    C) 188.4 cm^2 D) 75.4 cm^2

3) Find the surface area of a cylinder with radius 6 cm and height 8 cm. Use 3.14 for π. Round to the nearest tenth.

11-9 Volumes of Cylinders

1) Find the volume of a can with a diameter of 14 cm and height of 6 cm. Use 3.14 for π.

   A) 3,692.64 cm^3 B) 1,846.32 cm^3
   C) 65.94 cm^3 D) 923.16 cm^3

2) Solve.
   Amanda has a bottle shaped like a cylinder. It has a radius of 3 cm and height of 7 cm. Find how much the bottle will hold. Use 3.14 for π. Round to the nearest tenth.

   A) 197.8 cm^3 B) 65.9 cm^3
   C) 131.9 cm^3 D) 395.6 cm^3

3) Find the volume of a cylinder with radius 5 in. and height 6 in. Use 3.14 for π. Round to the nearest tenth.

11C Transformations

11-10 Translations

1) Point A is at (4, –2). Use the rule $(x, y) \rightarrow (x - 2, y + 1)$ to find the coordinates of A$'$.

   A) (6, –3)   B) (6, –1)   C) (2, –3)   D) (2, –1)

2) Use the rule $(x, y) \rightarrow (x + 5, y - 4)$ to find the coordinates of $\triangle A'B'C'$ if A = (–4, 2); B = (3, 2); C = (1, 3).

3) Use the rule $(x, y) \rightarrow (x, y + 5)$ to find the coordinates of $\triangle D'E'F'$ if D = (3, 0); E = (3, 4); F = (–2, 1)

4) Write a rule for the translation "left 5, up 3."

   A) $(x, y) \rightarrow (x + 5, y + 3)$ B) $(x, y) \rightarrow (x - 5, y - 3)$
   C) $(x, y) \rightarrow (x - 5, y + 3)$ D) $(x, y) \rightarrow (x + 5, y - 3)$

5)   Write a rule for the translation "left 3, down 7."

6)   Write a rule for the translation "right 4, down 3."

11–11 Reflections and Line Symmetry

1)   Which is a line of symmetry for the figure?

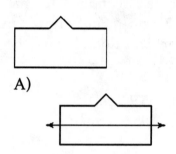

A)

B)

C)

D) Not here

2)   Which is not a line of symmetry for the figure?

A)

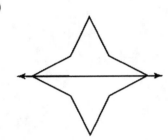

B)

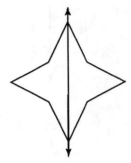

C)

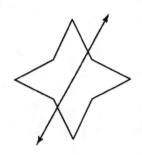

D) Not here

3)   The figure below has at least one line of symmetry.
Draw the line or lines of symmetry.

4)   Draw a reflection of the figure across the x–axis.

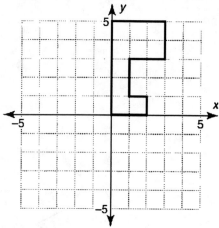

5)   Draw a reflection of the figure across the x–axis.

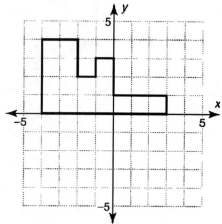

6)   Draw a reflection of the figure across the y–axis.

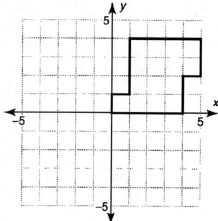

11–12 Rotations and Rotational Symmetry

1)   Does the figure have rotational symmetry? If it does, name all clockwise fractional turns that rotate the figure onto itself.

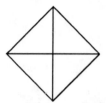

2)   Does the figure have rotational symmetry? If it does, name all clockwise fractional turns that rotate the figure onto itself.

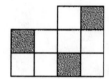

3)   Which figure below has rotational symmetry?

A) 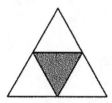   B)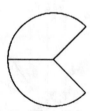

C) 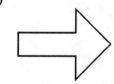   D)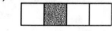

4)   How far has the figure on the left been rotated to get the figure on the right?

A) 180°   B) 30°   C) 60°   D) 90°

5) The figure on the left was rotated clockwise to the position shown on the right. How far was the figure rotated?

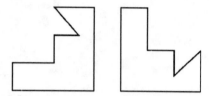

6) The figure on the left was rotated clockwise to the position shown on the right. How far was the figure rotated?

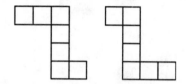

7) Give the coordinates of the vertices of this figure when it is rotated 180° clockwise.

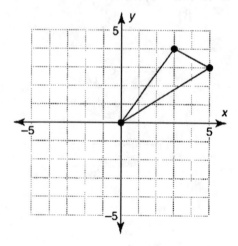

8) Give the coordinates of the vertices of this figure when it is rotated 90° clockwise.

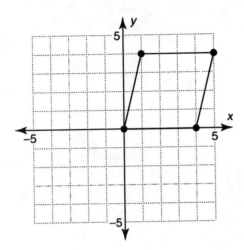

9) Draw △A′B′C′ by rotating △ABC 270° clockwise.

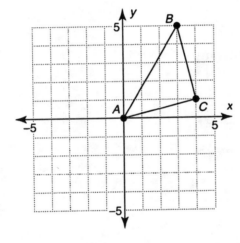

Chapter 11 Geometry

11A Polyhedrons

11-1 Exploring Polyhedrons

   1)   Answer: A

   2)   Answer: D

   3)   Answer: C

   4)   Answer:

   5)   Answer:

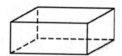

   6)   Answer: B

11-2 Isometric and Orthographic Drawing

   1)   Answer: B

   2)   Answer:

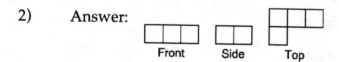

   3)   Answer:

   4)   Answer:

   5)   Answer: D

   6)   Answer: B

   7)   Answer: B

   8)   Answer: C

9)   Answer:

11–3 Polyhedron Nets and Surface Areas
1)   Answer: C

2)   Answer: D

3)   Answer: D

11–4 Volumes of Prisms
1)   Answer: C

2)   Answer: B

3)   Answer: A

11B Circles and Cylinders
11–5 Circles and Circle Graphs
1)   Answer: B

2)   Answer: B

3)   Answer: B

11–6 Pi and Circumference
1)   Answer: A

2)   Answer: A

3)   Answer: A

4)   Answer: B

5)   Answer: A

6)   Answer: D

11–7 Area of a Circle
1)   Answer: B

2)   Answer: B

3)   Answer: $3{,}850\ m^2$

11-8 Surface Areas of Cylinders

1)   Answer: C

2)   Answer: C

3)   Answer: 527.5 cm^2

11-9 Volumes of Cylinders

1)   Answer: D

2)   Answer: A

3)   Answer: 471.0 cm^3

11C Transformations

11-10 Translations

1)   Answer: D

2)   Answer: (1, –2); (8, –2); (6, –1)

3)   Answer: (3, 5); (3, 9); (–2, 6)

4)   Answer: C

5)   Answer: $(x, y) \rightarrow (x - 3, y - 7)$

6)   Answer: $(x, y) \rightarrow (x + 4, y - 3)$

11-11 Reflections and Line Symmetry

1)   Answer: C

2)   Answer: A

3)   Answer:

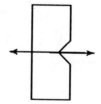

4)   Answer:

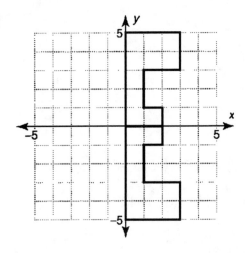

5)   Answer:

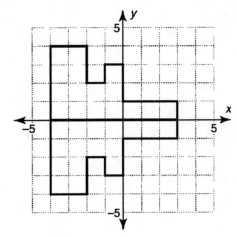

6)   Answer:

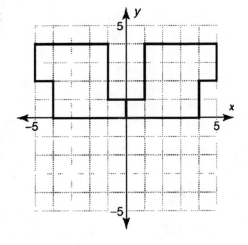

11–12 Rotations and Rotational Symmetry

1)   Answer: Yes; 1/4, 1/2, 3/4

2)   Answer: No

3)   Answer: A

4)   Answer: D

5)   Answer: 90°

6)   Answer: 180°

7)   Answer: (0, 0); (–3, –4); (–5, –3)

8)   Answer: (0, 0); (4, –1); (0, –4); (4, –5)

9)   Answer:

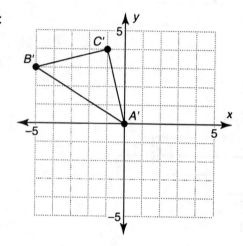

Chapter 12 Counting and Probability

Section 12A Counting

12-1   Counting Methods

1)   Sam's snack Bar offers 8 different sandwiches, 3 types of fruits, 5 types of crackers, and 3 types of cheese for box lunches. Find all possible combinations of box lunches that can be chosen.

   A) 19   B) 120   C) 45   D) 360

2)   A soccer team wants to select a new uniform. There are 9 different styles of shirts and 8 different styles of shorts. How many different uniform styles are there?

   A) 17   B) 117   C) 720   D) 72

3)   A yogurt shop offers smoothies made from 6 fruits, 4 flavors of yogurt, and 5 juices. How many different smoothies can be selected?

   A) 30   B) 120   C) 24   D) 20

4)   Fitness 2000 Health Club offers 4 different aerobic classes and 2 different aquacise classes. If none of the class times overlap, how many different ways can a member take both classes?

12-2   Arrangements

1)   In how many different orders can 7 pictures be arranged across a shelf?
   A) 49   B) 14   C) 720   D) 5,040

2)   How many 3-digit numbers can be made from the digits 4-9? No digit may be repeated.

3)   How many ways can 4 plants be placed on a display from a selection of 7 possible plants?
   A) 24   B) 840   C) 28   D) 3

4) How many ways can you arrange 9 different books?
A) 362,880   B) 81,000   C) 81   D) 40,320

5) How many different 3-letter combinations can be made from 9 different letters if no letters are repeated?
A) 720   B) 6   C) 504   D) 27

6) There are 6 people standing in line for the moves. In how many different ways can they stand?

7) Calculate 8!
A) 40,320   B) 64
C) 5040   D) Not here

8) Calculate 5!

9) In how many different arrangements can a group of 5 people sit in a row of 5 seats at a concert?

A) 25   B) 120   C) 24   D) 5

12–3   Choosing a Group

1) A balloon shop is offering a special bouquet. Customers may choose any 3 of the 7 available colors for their balloon bouquets. How many combinations of 3 colors are there?

A) 21   B) 210   C) 35   D) 4

2) There are 6 students competing for 2 spots on the debate team. How many different ways are there to choose 2 of the 6?

A) 24   B) 8   C) 80,640   D) 15

3) Pizza Palace offers any 3 of 8 available toppings on a pizza. How many different choices of 3 toppings are there?

4) How many ways can 6 students representatives be chosen from a group of 9 students?

A) 3   B) 15   C) 84   D) 54

5) Natural Foods sandwich stop offers only 1 type of bread, but customers can choose any 2 of the 8 available salads. How many different combinations of 2 salads are there?

Section 12B Chance and Probability

12-4   Odds and Fairness

1) A bag contains 2 blue markers, 6 red markers, and 5 black markers. What are the possible outcomes for choosing 1 marker?

A) Black   B) Blue
C) Blue, red, or black   D) Red

2) There is one chance in six that the Hawks will win the tournament today. What are the odds that they will win?

A) 1:7   B) 1:3   C) 1:4   D) 1:5

3) Ron and Rita are playing a game with a spinner. The spinner has 3 congruent sections that are red, blue, and yellow. If Ron spins a red or a blue, he wins. If Rita spins a yellow, she wins. What are the odds that Rita will win?

A) 2:3   B) 2:1   C) 1:3   D) 1:2

4) Lea and Linus are playing a game. In their game, a six sided number cube (numbered 1-6) is rolled. If Lea rolls a number less than 4, she wins. If Linus rolls 4 or greater, he wins. Give each player's odds of winning. Then tell if the game is fair.

12-5 Probability

1) What is the probability of drawing a green marble from a bag containing 6 green marbles, 9 yellow marbles, and 5 blue marbles?

   A) 50%   B) 20%   C) 60%   D) 30%

2) The odds of an event are 2 : 7. What is the probability that the event will occur?

   A) $\dfrac{7}{9}$ B) $\dfrac{2}{7}$ C) $\dfrac{2}{9}$ D) $\dfrac{7}{2}$

3) The probability that an event will not happen is $\dfrac{2}{7}$.

   What is the probability that the event will happen?

   A) $\dfrac{2}{5}$ B) $\dfrac{5}{7}$ C) $\dfrac{5}{2}$ D) $\dfrac{2}{9}$

4) Give the probability of drawing a green balloon from a bag containing 5 green balloons and 5 yellow balloons as a fraction, a percent, and a decimal.

5) What is the probability of drawing a red crayon from a box containing 2 red crayons, 11 blue crayons, and 13 yellow crayons.

   A) $\dfrac{2}{13}$ B) $\dfrac{9}{26}$ C) $\dfrac{11}{13}$ D) $\dfrac{1}{13}$

12-6 Experimental Probability

1) Nicole drew a marble from a bag of marbles 100 times, replacing her selection each time. If her draws included 38 clear marbles and 22 blue marbles, What is the experimental probability of drawing a clear or blue marble?

2) Vinh drew a coin from a bag of coins 100 times, replacing her selection each time. If her draws included 42 pennies and 20 nickels, what is the experimental probability of drawing a penny or a nickel?

3) Esperanza drew a ticket from a bag of different colored tickets 100 times, replacing her selection each time. If her draws included 45 blue tickets and 30 red tickets, What is the experimental probability of drawing a red or blue ticket?

4) Tyrone drew a coin from a bag of change 100 times, replacing his selection each time. If Tyrone drew 24 pennies and 10 dimes, what is the experimental probability of drawing a penny or a dime?

A) 0.24   B) 3.4   C) 0.34   D) 2.4

5) Julie drew a marker from a box of markers 100 times, replacing her selection each time. If Julie's draws included 8 black markers and there are no brown markers in the box, what is the experimental probability of drawing a black marker or a brown marker?

A) $\dfrac{80}{100}$

B) $\dfrac{8}{100}$ or $\dfrac{2}{25}$

C) $\dfrac{40}{100}$

D) Not here

6) If a coin lands randomly on the board shown, what is the geometric probability that it will land in the shaded region?

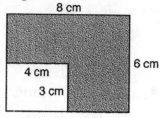

A) $\dfrac{1}{4}$ B) $\dfrac{3}{4}$ C) $\dfrac{1}{2}$ D) $\dfrac{4}{5}$

7) A board is divided into 64 smaller squares: 16 black and 48 red. What is the geometric probability that a marker dropped randomly on the board will fall on a black square?

8) What is the geometric probability that a ring tossed randomly on the circle will land on red?

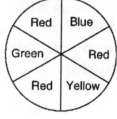

A) 60%   B) 75%   C) 30%   D) 50%

9) If a coin lands randomly on the board shown, what is the geometric probability that it will land in the shaded region?

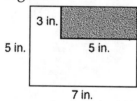

12–7   Independent and Dependent Events

1) Sam drew a marble from a box. He then drew another one after replacing the first. Are his results for the two draws *independent* or *dependent* events?

2) Two chess clubs have consecutive matches against each other. Is the outcome of the second match *independent* of the outcome of the first match, or *dependent* on its outcome?

A) Clearly independent
B) Somewhat dependent, somewhat independent
C) Clearly dependent
D) Neither dependent nor independent

3) Olivia draws three coins from a bag of loose change. If no replacements were made, which statement best describes the three draws?

A) They are independent.
B) In certain cases, they are dependent.
C) They are neither dependent nor independent.
D) They are dependent.

4) Adam rolls a number cube and spins a spinner. Are the events independent or dependent?

5) Robin draws a ball from a bag that contains 4 white balls and 6 yellow balls. She then draws a second ball without replacing the first. What is the probability that both balls Robin draws are white?

6) A spinner is divided into four congruent sections, numbered 1 through 4. What is the probability of spinning two 3s in a row?

A) $\dfrac{1}{3}$ B) $\dfrac{1}{16}$ C) $\dfrac{1}{4}$ D) $\dfrac{1}{9}$

7) Taylor picked 2 marbles from a bowl containing 4 red, 2 green, and 5 blue marbles. If no replacements were made, what is the probability that both of Taylor's marbles are blue?

A) $\dfrac{5}{11}$ B) $\dfrac{2}{11}$ C) $\dfrac{5}{22}$ D) $\dfrac{9}{11}$

8)   Ben tossed two six-sided number cubes (each numbered 1-6) at the same time. Find P(1, 6).

9)   Heidi tossed a coin and spun a spinner divided into 4 congruent sections, numbered 1–4, at the same time. What is P(heads, 2)?

A) $\dfrac{1}{6}$ B) $\dfrac{1}{8}$ C) $\dfrac{1}{4}$ D) $\dfrac{1}{16}$

Chapter 12 Counting and Probability

Section 12A Counting

12-1   Counting Methods

1)   Answer: D

2)   Answer: D

3)   Answer: B

4)   Answer: 8

12-2   Arrangements

1)   Answer: D

2)   Answer: 120

3)   Answer: B

4)   Answer: A

5)   Answer: C

6)   Answer: 720

7)   Answer: A

8)   Answer: 120

9)   Answer: B

12-3   Choosing a Group

1)   Answer: C

2)   Answer: D

3)   Answer: 56

4)   Answer: C

5)   Answer: 28

Section 12B Chance and Probability

12-4 Odds and Fairness

1) Answer: C

2) Answer: D

3) Answer: D

4) Answer: 3:3; 3:3; yes

12-5 Probability

1) Answer: D

2) Answer: C

3) Answer: B

4) Answer: $\frac{5}{10}$; 50%; 0.5

5) Answer: D

12-6 Experimental Probability

1) Answer: $\frac{3}{5}$

2) Answer: $\frac{31}{50}$

3) Answer: $\frac{3}{4}$

4) Answer: C

5) Answer: B

6) Answer: B

7) Answer: $\frac{16}{64}$ or $\frac{1}{4}$

8) Answer: D

9)   Answer: $\dfrac{3}{7}$

12–7   Independent and Dependent Events

1)   Answer: Independent

2)   Answer: A

3)   Answer: D

4)   Answer: Independent

5)   Answer: $\dfrac{2}{15}$

6)   Answer: B

7)   Answer: B

8)   Answer: $\dfrac{1}{36}$

9)   Answer: B